GROWING UP AND DUCKING DOWN

Eric Armstrong

MINERVA PRESS

LONDON

MONTREUX   LOS ANGELES   SYDNEY

GROWING UP AND DUCKING DOWN
Copyright © Eric Armstrong 1997

All Rights Reserved

ISBN 1 86106 275 3

First Published 1997 by
MINERVA PRESS
195 Knightsbridge
London SW7 1RE

Printed in Great Britain by
Biddles Ltd, King's Lynn, Norfolk

GROWING UP AND
DUCKING DOWN

About The Author

Having practised, taught and written extensively about industrial relations, Emeritus Professor Eric Armstrong OBE, a highly experienced arbitrator, has recently branched out to become the author of works on other aspects of social history.

Contents

Chapter One
By The Fireside

"Sal, just listen to this a minute."

Wilf glanced across the sadly worn, badly faded, home-made hearth-rug towards his wife who sat facing him, her back to the sash window. Sal frowned, partly because she was absorbed in her knitting and partly because she sensed a hint of mischief in the tone of her husband's voice.

"Just keep quiet a minute you old donkey. You can see I'm counting stitches and I must get this pullover finished for Jimmy."

Moments later, she held out, at arm's length, the nearly completed front of the pullover, neatly knitted in ash grey wool. She scrutinised her handiwork with evident satisfaction.

"There, that seems to be all right but I hope I've got enough yellow and black wool left to edge the V neck with."

Yellow and black – the natty colours of Handsworth Grammar School. Sal certainly didn't want *her* son to be inferior in turn-out from other lads, many of whom obviously came from much posher homes, from up Handsworth Wood for example.

Placing wool and needles in a small, brown wicker basket on the 'cheap and nasty' lino (brazenly pretending to be parquet flooring) Sal leaned back in her shabby armchair. Settling her head comfortably against the dingy brown leatherette of one of the chair's wings, she closed her eyes, clasped her hands over her brightly flowered pinafore – and sighed;

"Fire away then – I suppose it's your old pal, that lovesick old monkey, Byron again."

Wilf chuckled but ventured no denial.

He unhooked his thumbs from the shallow pockets of his grey knitted waistcoat, bordered with Aston Villa's claret and blue, and picked up a sturdy looking book with drab grey-green covers. He eased himself into a comfortable reading position, placing his elbows on the wooden arms of the small, rickety easy chair generously padded with cushions. One more cushion, resting on a wooden footstool, supported his gammy leg parallel with the floor. The bottoms of his long underpants tucked tidily into the tops of his socks, Wilf wriggled the toes of his un-slippered right foot luxuriously in the cheerful warmth of the blazing coal fire.

Despite these cosy arrangements, Wilf remained slightly self-conscious – but determined. He tilted back his grey head, cleared his throat and in a pleasing baritone gave voice to some of Byron's best known lines;

" "She walks in beauty, like the night
Of cloudless climes and starry skies
And all that's best of dark and bright..." "

Wilf paused and looked ironically at his wife whose fair hair was fading and thinning...

" "Meet in her aspect and her eyes:" "

Sal gave a disdainful sniff and resumed her knitting.

"Hm. I don't suppose your precious Black Beauty ever knitted a pair of socks like those you've got on. Beauty's only skin deep – and knitting on four needles takes some doing you know."

"So you've told me before. But there must be room for romance as well."

Wilf promptly launched into increasingly wavering song,

" " 'Tis the last r-o--se of Summer..." "

"I want that sung at my funeral you know."

"Hallelujah, that'll be the day – there's plenty of life left in you yet, you old donkey."

"I do hope you're right Mrs Caudle. Until that happy day, how about...?" – and he began another song:

" "I dreamt I dwelt in marble halls.
With vassals and serfs by my side..." "

At this point Wilf winked knowingly at his wife for the heavy emphasis on 'vassals and serfs' signified to those in the know: 'just put the kettle on Sal and brew a pot of steaming golden brown.'

The wink remained ignored as Sal's busy needles clicked away. Then, with another row finished, she remarked:

"Just put the kettle on son, will you? Count John McCormack there is thirsty again."

Jimmy rose awkwardly from his seat at the square dining table where he had been making scant progress with his homework and impots during his father's poetry reading and song recital.

"Oh blas...!"

Jim half-stifled the curse but his mother turned her head sharply, remonstrating:

"Now then, that's not the sort of language I want to hear from a grammar school boy."

"Sorry – I just caught my shin against this" – he paused – "bloomin' monstrosity" – he pointed to the offending piece of furniture – "right where I've still got a big bruise from playing football."

"I don't like you playing that nasty rough game," murmured his mother.

Muttering and shin rubbing, Jimmy disappeared into the tiny, neat, but poorly equipped kitchen.

Just why had his quirky dad taken it into his quirky noddle to accept from a retired doctor (for whom Wilf's even quirkier, beaky nosed sister Ruby had kept house) a heavy, monstrously cumbersome roll-top oak desk? This monstrosity seemed malevolently purpose-built for shin barking, elbow and hip knocking. Apart from supporting the Bakelite wireless on its top, the desk was of no practical use that he could see; for his dad perhaps, who hid unwelcome bills among the various drawers and pigeon holes. Just the ticket such a desk, for impressing working class patients 'on the panel' in a doctor's surgery in the 1920s and 30s – but now, in 1938 it appeared wildly out of place in his new home.

'New' home. That was a laugh! Jimmy turned on the single tap over the shallow, brownstone sink, filled the kettle with chilled water, lit a gas ring – and shivered. Crikey! what a dump: the kitchen, the house, the garden, the new circumstances. Inwardly he raged with frustration and anger. Yet, he didn't blame his parents for the family's recent slide down the social scale. No, he blamed capitalism and fate – whatever that might be.

Again he shivered; the kitchen, cold and dank was permeated with the damp of thousands of washdays and hundreds of thousands of turns of the wooden rollers of cast iron framed mangles. With more turns to come – of that he was sure – and he would be doing much of the turning. Another shiver and he returned to the warmth and brightness of the living room, taking care to give the roll-top sufficient clearance.

Crikey, another dump. Nothing in the greatly overcrowded room was new. Nothing sparkled, except the spotless windows and the brass fire-irons. All the non-matching pieces of furniture bore the scratches, scars and stains of previous ownership.

Jim resumed his seat at the table, picked up his J-nibbed pen and snorted violently.

"Be careful you don't upset the ink bottle dear. I'm sure it will all work out all right in the end."

A gentle lady, his mother, highly competent in household affairs – but sometimes such an unworldly optimist. What could he tell her of his headache inducing problems with algebra, geometry and physics when he understood relatively little about these subjects himself, subjects totally alien to his parents' experience? And what would his Dad say, if his help was sought? Very little that was relevant Jim thought. Wilf would doubtless tilt his head back, assume a highly sagacious aldermanic air, clear his throat and most probably pronounce, 'Well, there's nothing in *Childe Harold* about it.' Then a pet phrase would clinch matters: 'Fair play's a jewel you know.'

With cups of "steaming golden brown" now being sipped with evident relish, relative silence prevailed in the room, the fire crackling cheerily, the sipping barely audible.

Jimmy fell to musing, stabbing viciously now and then at a Physics homework question.

"Explain how you would use a Wheatstone's bridge to measure the resistance of a wire.

A wire of length 2 metres and cross-section 1 sq. mm...?"

He felt tempted to ask his dad whether, in all his exotic travels, Childe Harold had ever crossed a Wheatstone Bridge – but thought better of it. He knew the 'proper old Victorian' wouldn't be best pleased at being the butt of grammar school 'wit.' Moreover Jimmy sensed that his Dad didn't quite know what to make of his youngest child, the 'brainy one', the first of his family to attend a grammar school.

As Wilf was always ready to remind anyone, he, along with his classmates, had left school at the age of twelve, way back in 1890 – starting paid employment as an errand boy. His other four sons and his daughter had received the customary elementary schooling and,

John apart, they weren't doing too badly in life. Phil drove a Corporation bus. When he could find work, Alec applied his joinery skills, while Ted, like his Dad before him, set precious stones and pastes in jewellery in one of the Dickensian workshops of the dingy warren known as the Jewellery Quarter. Young May, winsome, wayward and light-hearted, had captivated a devoted slave for a husband who managed a local hardware shop.

But Jim, half brother to the former widower's brood, remained a puzzle. What, Wilf would like to know, would Jimmy actually do when he had finished his expensive education? By Wilf's standards, expensive that education certainly was, even with the 'top weight' means tested local authority maintenance grant taken into account. Perhaps the youngster would do some clerking, become a teacher even. Anyway, Sal would see to things for her 'only chick.'

That 'chick' of the bruised shin, now nearly fifteen, still sat at the table scratching – with his pen, and at his head, generously covered with thick, slightly wavy dark brown hair – bristly short cut, back and sides.

"Oh, do leave your nits alone James," a hint of exasperation in the gentle rebuke from his mother.

"Sorry."

Jimmy stopped scratching – for quite half a minute.

"Just thinking."

He often was, being essentially a serious minded boy, though not without a good sense of humour or the occasional ability to engage in sharp repartee. Still, as he admitted to himself, he was prone to spells of musing, of daydreaming, of wondering – often all mixed oddly together. Why, for instance, did none of the women in his family and those he heard talked about, have normal feet? 'Can't get a pair of shoes to fit me,' came the frequent wailing and wincing refrain.

Then again, why had his mother married a widower fourteen years older than herself (a match strongly opposed by her own family) and taken on, (assiduously and lovingly at that!) the role of stepmother with the eldest stepson but seven years younger than herself? From scraps of information he had gleaned, Jimmy constructed an explanation, reasonably satisfactory to himself, but one he didn't dare discuss with his parents.

For the umpteenth time he went over that explanation. His mom's true love had been killed in the Great War and, to his knowledge, Sal was a woman brimful of deep maternal feelings and impulses. In years past, she had been desperate to bear and rear a child of her own. Snapshots helped to strengthen the impression that, at twenty nine she had been a slim, pretty blonde with fine spun hair, a smooth, pale rose schoolgirl complexion, who bore some resemblance around the mouth and eyes to Bette Davis, the great cinema star. Yes, especially around the eyes which protruded slightly. 'Thyroid trouble you know,' said the knowing, nodding black crow ladies of her acquaintance.

Wilf, a widower on the lookout for a competent, loving housekeeper/wife/foster mother met Sally, (Jimmy never knew the circumstances) and they married. Neither parent seemed to regret what must have been, to some extent, in Jimmy's opinion at least, a marriage of convenience.

"Penny for your thoughts son."

Jimmy flushed slightly but answered glibly enough.

"Oh, just wondering whether Villa will do much good this year."

"Fat chance." Wilf's voice was full of scorn. "They're not a patch on the pre-war sides with Howard Spencer and Harry Hampton. "Prince of Full Backs" was Howard Spencer. And what about Charlie Athersmith – like greased lightning down the touch-line he was and..."

"Yes Dad, you've told us so before about how he put up an umbrella when playing in a rainstorm and James needs to get on with his homework."

Jim's thoughts drifted to another villa, a true First Division villa, No. 96, "the old house" of his Schoolboy's Diary.

Now, No. 96 had been something like a house and a home. It had style and standing had No. 96. All right, that home was also a terraced, brick house, and only gas-lit – but one of four storeys, if you included the dank, dark, evil smelling cellar where pennies slotted into the voracious gas meter. From the attic window, the tall trees atop Barr Beacon could be clearly seen. In between these highs and lows lay three bedrooms and, on the ground floor – a front room, a middle room, a kitchen and a kitchen scullery – all linked to a long, tiled hall.

Yes, that house revealed signs of past greatness, of lower middle class prosperity and social respectability. A visitor entering by the elaborately grained front door, (a tribute to painters' skills with steel combs, rags, thumb dabs, brown and yellow paints) would step, not into the hall, but, mark you, a vestibule where the inner door stood welcoming and resplendent, proud of its panes of glowing ruby red, deep blue and emerald glass.

In the dining room, at the side of the handsome fireplace, an ornate, metal handle, curved in shape, was fixed to the wall. When pulled round, a bell would, in gracious living days, have pealed in the kitchen to summon some long forgotten skivvy to her condescending employers' presence. This room also flaunted elegant French windows which opened into a rockery resplendent with arching dark green ferns, redolent of Victorian respectability.

Best of all – and this really was a touch of class – the house boasted a bathroom and indoor lav, splendid things which the new home lamentably lacked.

Jimmy understood well enough why the family had moved from such relative magnificence to the present dismal, out at elbows, hard-up, just above the poverty line: dump. In two words – economic necessity – and in four: a deeply exasperated landlord. (Such a touchy chap about rent arrears!)

At No. 96 family numbers had steadily dwindled. In turn, Phil, Alec and Ted married and moved away – naturally enough to rented accommodation – and then to council houses on the fast expanding estate dubbed by bus conductors as 'bleedin' Siberia.' (Arctic wind swept Kingstanding.) Finally, May, the youngest, flew the coop with her devoted Bill and their toddler Bob.

As the numbers at 96 went down, so did the income. Wilf had never been a steady, reliable wage earner. Trained as a gem setter, he was no master craftsman and the demand for jewellery could be wildly variable. So Wilf worked for this firm and for that, for longer or shorter periods, in Birmingham's ramshackle Jewellery Quarter. Sometimes he became an out-worker, when the oddly shaped workbench of the jeweller would be set up in Jim's parents' bedroom.

Jim recalled that while still quite a small boy, he had temporarily lost his Dad who disappeared into hospital for major surgery to his right leg. Osteomyelitis had attacked the knee joint. No wonder drugs in the 1920s, but amputation was averted, at a high price, great gashes of wounds that never fully healed, periodic and painful inflammation, and a permanently stiff leg.

Nearly a full year's lay-off from work had done nothing, in the late 1920s to improve Wilf's chances of regular employment.

So now, in 1938, and close to his sixtieth birthday, Wilf had no regular employment income. He did receive a small state pension as 'paltry compensation' for his eldest son having been blown to bloody bits in Flanders. But for Wilf, that payment formed no part of the family income, belonging entirely to John's father as John's mother was dead. All those events were pre-Sal history.

Arguably, such a stance was a harsh one but Jimmy dared never to mention it. When the issue was very occasionally raised by Sal, her husband became disagreeably defensive, usually terminating ill tempered exchanges with: 'It's got nothing to do with you and that's final.' Whatever else it may have been, Jimmy took this attitude to be a clear indication of the bitterness felt by Wilf at the death of his first, and probably favourite son.

Then, of course, there was the dole to swell the income and raise the standard of living to one of threadbare solvency. Jim had not experienced real hunger but was well accustomed to bread and scrape, bubble and squeak, faggots and peas, stews, with any treats, a tin of pineapple chunks perhaps, reserved for Sundays. Wardrobes remained meagre, well patched and darned. As far as underwear and shirts were concerned, Army principles applied – one on, one off and one in the wash.

But no surplus money for holidays – no siree. In fact, Jim had never experienced a family holiday with his parents. A day or two away, at the homes of relatives, or in the country with cousins, aunts and uncles. Until 1937 – and buxom Brenda.

"Why are you frowning so son?"

The knitting needles had stopped their clicking.

"Oh, just recalling a few memories about 96."

His mother gave a significant glance at her husband who shrugged his shoulders but said nothing.

"What's done is done. Don't dwell on it. Don't let it spoil things at school – and do get on with your homework – and whatever else you have to do."

Jim made a determined stab at copying more lines as one of the impositions he had received that week. In one Maths lesson alone he had been told "five times", so his diary recorded, "to sit up straight."

In an act of long range defiance, Jimmy slumped on his chair and allowed more memories from the past fourteen years at 96 to race pell mell into his mind. And to quote his favourite author, P. G. Wodehouse, what spiffing memories!

Jasper the black cat with his head stuck in an empty salmon tin: the wedding reception for flapper cousin Dolly when tipsy Bertie crashed a jigging Charleston foot through the big drum: the sobs of disappointment at not being able to play for his mom the new tune he had so determinedly practised on his mouth-organ. After long hours charring in a dairy, 'to make ends meet', his mom had been far too bone weary to even want to listen to her chick's achievement. With Ken, his best friend, pouring molten lead from a saucepan into sand moulds to cast speedway bikes and their riders: implementing a 'wizard wheeze' from a boy's comic by hanging from a washing line, a mixture of old pop and milk bottles partly filled with varying amounts of water. After numerous adjustments to the volumes, musical notes could eventually be struck by tapping the bottles with the back of an old dessert spoon. The resourceful boy's xylophone al fresco. 'The Bells of St. Mary's' had rung out quite appealingly (Ho! Ho!) from by the lilac tree.

Ferrying battered toy soldiers up the winding Amazon masquerading as the path between the banks of ferns running from the French windows: enjoying the blasphemy and discomfiture of his brother-in-law who had, by his habit of sniffing at every object handled, broken the skin of a hot rice pudding – and burned his nose quite badly. Ah, such truly spiffing memories!

Then came the summer of 1937, Coronation year, when his mom's two younger and unmarried brothers, Les and Harold, had taken him away- for his first real holiday, his first sight of the sea – for a whole, thrilling fortnight, to Babbacombe, Torquay. His first experience of coastal beauties, and one particular beauty, the boarding house landlady's daughter, bonny, bouncing Brenda.

Although shy, painfully so at times, Jimmy had become quite interested in girls. But he had only mixed with them as kids in the same class at elementary school, and artlessly with his many cousins in the Black Country. But with bouncy Brenda had begun that period of wondering how best to proceed with the opposite sex of his own age, who had taken on a more interesting shape and appearance than their juniors.

He was still wondering as he sat at that dining table in February 1938.

Girls at primary school had simply been facts of life, kids who dressed differently, giggled a lot and whispered a great deal among themselves, but took no interest in exciting games of football, conkers, marbles or playing at English and Jerries. The sight of dashing pilots in their squadrons of Sopwith Camels, Spads and Fokkers, wheeling around with arms outstretched to simulate wings, shrilly pitched machine guns chattering – left the girls completely unmoved as they concentrated on hop-scotch, skipping and giggling.

Suddenly, during morning playtime one day, all that changed, if briefly. It was not Armistice Day but 18th October 1929 when everyone stood stock still. Shrill squealing and childish babble suddenly, dramatically, replaced by a silence almost tangible. Goggle eyes stared skywards.

Moving slowly and in a slanting line away from the playground 'aerial' dogfight, a massive torpedo shaped 'zeppelin' glided silently over Handsworth rooftops and chimneys. The mighty airship R 101 was undertaking a second trial flight from Cardington. Eerily noiseless, the majestic airship drifted from view. Fokkers and Camels resumed their noisy scrap with refreshed clamour and vigour. Giggling and whispering returned at higher pitch levels.

Jim had always enjoyed his visits to the Black Country relatives who sensibly called girls: wenches. Most of these wenches had been tom-boys at heart, especially those from a large family of eleven, who lived in a low sprawling house of many odd shaped rooms, bordered by a cobbled yard, high walls, barns and stables. The ever present awareness of cart-horses, harness and hay, the proximity of canals, barges and numerous patches of wasteland, all tended to make for free spirited games and escapades.

But now these wenches had passed into double figures, in age, they seemed steadily to lose their tomboy zip. Extrovert boisterousness had increasingly given way to greater self-consciousness, concern for appearance and lively chat about fashion, gigolo type film stars and 'hair-dos.' At least Jim had learned that Friday nights were 'out' for dating. All the civilised world knew that "Friday night is Amami Night", shampoo and whatever, certainly spicy gossip.

Somehow hoydens had turned into – well, Jimmy wasn't entirely sure what was meant by – 'nice young ladies.' Still, he knew well enough that the happy go lucky, free and easy days with girl cousins were over. A new relationship had to be evolved. Even more baffling when girls, or wenches, were at the outset, strangers, like busty Babbacombe Brenda for instance.

At the recollection of Brenda his mood took a further downward swing for he strongly suspected that Brenda's interest in him was largely due to the interest Brenda's mother had shown in his bachelor Uncle Harold. Wimmin! Or, put more poetically, "Frailty, thy name is woman!" He gave a deep sigh and an irritable wave of his hand that nearly upset the ink bottle.

"Steady son – you'll get things right if you persevere."

Jim leaned back on his chair, groaning inwardly. He was very ready to persevere (if need be like the fellow in the Oxo advert: "Percy Vere – with Oxo." Ho! Ho!) But what he really needed was imaginative technical help. No-one in the family could provide it. A grammar school education constituted totally uncharted waters. At times such an education hardly seemed worth all the fag involved. And why, oh why (pullovers and socks apart) couldn't more things be new for a change. Football boots for example. Too often these hand-me-downs, (a strange phrase to apply to footwear he thought) were ill-fitting, badly scuffed, with soft toe-caps, and too quickly porous.

To lighten his spirits Jimmy surreptitiously glanced at the folded 1937 copy of *Modern Wonder* that lay partly concealed under his right elbow. The brightly coloured cover showed a line of aircraft flying over what appeared to be four giant loudspeakers mounted on a flat truck. "The Ears of the Air Force. Wonderful machines that pick up the approach of enemy planes many miles away."

'Would there be air raids on Britain one day?' he wondered.

A brisk rat-a-tat sounded at the front door.

Contemplating air raids, Jimmy nearly jumped out of his skin. His mother, also startled, but for a different reason, anxiously called out:

"Just see who that is son, will you? If it's the insurance man, tell him he'll get his money without fail, next month!"

Jim rose, his head now swimming with thoughts of submarine warfare. He slipped round the draught excluder curtain and entered the air lock. On his right, an unlit step down into an open space under the staircase, the pantry, its earthen floor only partly covered by a roughly cut piece of lino. He pressed on and opened a door.

Chapter Two
Saturday Evening – and Most of Sunday

Stepping into the chilly front room cleared Jimmy's head of naval fantasies. In this 'parlour' even the battered, sagging chesterfield, with its cabbage roses patterned loose covers, seemed clammy to the touch. 'Roll on Christmas, let's have some nuts – and a roaring fire in the grate.' He smiled wryly and, as he usually did on entering the room, glanced across at a sepia coloured portrait hanging above the empty fireplace.

From within a large, oval, mahogany frame (a few scarlet poppies at its rim) a bright eyed, smiling young man looked out upon the world with the confidence that typifies the healthy 20 year old. In army uniform, he wore a bandoleer across his chest: the half brother Jimmy had never known, except by hearsay.

Gunner John Norton, killed 5th September, 1918 whose grave "was never found and identified", and just one "of some 9,900 officers and men who lost their lives in this area and who have no known place of burial."

Would he have liked this brother? Jimmy wondered. Most probably. John was talked of in the family as having been a fine runner – something Jim longed to be. He moved to the front door, pressed down a piece of cracked lino with his foot and pulled aside the shabby door length curtain that served as a would be draught excluder (no vestibule in this dump) and glumly let in the damp, chill air of a February early evening.

"Wotcher."

"Wotcher."

Ken, silhouetted for a moment against the garish light of the fish and chip shop opposite, stepped lightly over the doorstep and the door was closed.

"Are you coming out for a bit?"

"Dunno really."

"Why not?"

"I've got piles of Physics, Geometry and Algebra homework and impots to finish."

"Do them tomorrow."

Jimmy pondered, not just because of the homework and impots but because he strongly suspected that Ken would be wanting to chase after bits of fluff again, and Jim certainly didn't feel in a bird chasing mood.

Ken was a tall, fair-haired, fresh complexioned lad, a good athlete, an exuberant extrovert who thought quite highly of himself and of his bird snaring appeal. He and Jim had been friends since primary school days and had remained so even after Ken had gone to Aston Grammar School to play with a strange egg-shaped ball.

Jim continued to ponder for he knew that in continuing to scratch away at homework and impots, he would probably spoil his parents' full enjoyment of the mirthful Saturday evening wireless programme. His ice-box bedroom couldn't possibly be used as a study. That clinched it.

"OK then, I'll just get my coat."

"Don't be late son, back before ten remember?"

The two friends walked off into the winter murk.

"Let's go up Stamford Road shall we? It'll make a change."

"Okey Dokey."

What Jim hadn't disclosed was his reluctance to walk past his old home in Crompton Road. Ken, lucky devil, could afford to be gracious for he lived in one of the very few modern houses in that road – a house that actually possessed not only a front lawn, and a flower border – but space for a garage as well.

The friends walked steadily upwards to Putney Road, pausing a moment to look at Chiles', the well-stocked corner grocer shop.

"Remember Mr Collins?"

"Not 'alf. He was a real tartar he was."

Indeed he had been. Tall, slim and gaunt, Mr Collins had seemed as knobbly thin and whippy as the cane he brought crashing down on to the desk lids of those young scholars judged to be inattentive or lazy.

"Yes, sometimes he used to send me to get pieces of cheese from Chiles'."

Once more Jimmy saw himself hurdling back to school in the style of Sunny Jim who, according to the cereal advert in the shop window, enjoyed soaring good health.

"High o'er the fence leaps Sunny Jim

Force is the food that raises him."

A few moments later the friends paused again – outside their old school in Westminster Road.

"I wonder what happened to Fatty Dudley?"

Ronald Dudley hadn't really been fat but tall for his age, awkwardly built certainly, a clumsy mover and bespectacled – a natural scorer for the School's cricket eleven of 1934.

"You were a bit of a rabbit at cricket, weren't you Jim?"

Ken, from his lofty eminence as captain, first rate batsman, bowler and fielder was well placed to say so. But the remark stung. Sensing resentment, Ken continued with affable condescension: "But that was quite a good speech of yours when you and Joan Higgins made a farewell presentation to Mr Messiter," a reference to the retirement of their silvery haired, widely revered headmaster.

At the top of Westminster Road, the boys crossed into Heathfield Road, pausing a third time to gawp with a mixture of admiration, wonderment and envy, at the fine toys on display in a newsagent's shop.

A few years earlier, Jim had diligently squirrelled away for month after month, in a Christmas Club Fund: twopences, threepenny bits, the occasional tanner – until, until – the magical total of 14s 6d had been reached and recorded in that exciting, red covered savings card. Then, ah then! the magnificent stationary steam engine, a Bowman would you believe, became his. To be shared of course with his brother-in-law. With Bill's help (non-sniffing on these occasions) and enthusiastic guidance, he had been able to power, in splendidly spluttering, hissing, vibrating style, various Meccano models he had codged together.

Now began the gentle climb up Heathfield Road to Villa Cross. Ken started to look about him more keenly while Jim's attention seemed to be caught more and more by the indifferent shine on the toe-caps of his well-worn black leather shoes.

The friends were nearing the start (or the finish) of a popular monkey run. At the Villa Cross picture house, where, so Jim had been told, it was 'great' to be with a girl on the back row, they turned left into Lozells Road. This extensive thoroughfare boasted long lines of busy, brightly lit shops, on both sides of the road, especially towards the Aston end. A Woolworth's store, and a picture house added to the enticing delights on offer.

Up and down this bustling road, thronged with early evening shoppers, pairs of adolescent, and mostly self-conscious girls and boys sauntered and practised their clumsy social skills at 'picking up' or being 'picked up' by a fancied pair of the opposite gender.

Jimmy disliked this process intensely but curiosity, and loyalty to his friend, usually combined to subdue, if not overcome his embarrassment. 'Surely,' he thought, 'there must be better ways of getting to know a girl than this? After all, what sort of parents were they who allowed their daughters to roam the streets in this way? Or, more alarming still, what sort of daughters could they be if they were deceiving their parents as to their whereabouts?' Such thoughts troubled Jim but Ken appeared to suffer no such fastidious qualms. It seemed natural and instinctive with him to chase after girls, all girls, whatever the location or circumstances. And so he took the lead in making overtures and chatting up, and was not readily rebuffed either by silence, apparent disdain or waspish comment. His own self-esteem gave him great resilience.

Because of his enterprise and sheer cheek, both friends tacitly accepted that it was only right if Ken enjoyed first pick from any pair of girls with whom the friends happened to click. Neither then suspected that there might come a time when that established order of preference would be astoundingly overturned.

On this particular damp and chilly evening, bits of fluff were very thin on the pavements, and in the shop doorways peering at gaudy jewellery and fancy fashions.

"Ken, I'm getting fed up with this. It's getting too parky. I'm nipping into Woolies for a warm."

Jimmy plunged through the sturdy swing doors into the comforting fug of the store with its welcoming atmospheric mix of slightly stale, slightly over-heated air, the fragrance of cheap sweets and of cheap scents – and gently glowing humanity. Saturday evening shoppers seemed in no hurry to leave this cosy, brilliantly lit bazaar of nothing over sixpence necessities and delights. Ken and Jim dawdled round the highly polished, well laden counters for quite half an hour, sometimes together, sometimes apart. Good ogling practice for Ken, as many of the shop assistants seemed young and pretty – but perhaps above cradle snatching practices.

More than once Jim sidled past the counter where extensive rows of spectacles reflected glancing light and shade. Dare he try on one or two pairs when Ken wasn't looking? He knew that he probably needed glasses but as a sensitive, or vain (he wasn't sure which) schoolboy, he was still unwilling to face the taunting cries of: "Yah! Old four eyes!"

He fished into his left hand trouser pocket. Yes, his favourite penknife was still there – it had done some wonderful whittling in its time: so was an elastic band, a toffee wrapper, a crumpled cigarette card, a comb and a few coppers.

Twopence to spend – but on what? The temptations were positively fearsome. Pear drops, aniseed balls, liquorice allsorts, toffee, chocolate – would be shared and soon gone. He drifted, almost drooling, past the seductive sweets counter, then made for the display of out of date American magazines, many of them concerned with aviation. He picked out a favourite – *Flying Aces* and, largely because of its cover – the July 1937 issue.

In lurid colours an artist had painted flights of German bombers exploding as they crashed into a curtain of steel wires held aloft by barrage balloons. The caption read: "Death In The Nets Over London."

"Come on, I'm for home."

Ken, after a quick last look round to make sure he had not missed any enchantress, nodded his assent.

*

Before Jim had finished reading about the humorous World War I adventures of American flyer Phineas Pinkham in *Flying Aces*, it was suddenly Sunday afternoon and so, Sunday School again at the Congregational Church, with a special class for the half dozen older boys, Mr Martin 'in charge', of moral edification, in Bedlam.

In his own, long suffering way, Harry Martin was something of a Christian martyr. An affable bachelor, in his early thirties, a man with a ready beaming smile, Mr Martin seemed to see nothing but good in people; an arguably perilous and certainly optimistic approach to the schooling in sound moral behaviour of high spirited fourteen and fifteen year old lads. They played him up, not unmercifully, but over frequently and always noisily. With a bland, indulgent smile, Mr Martin always forgave.

A bored Jim fidgeted. 'Old Harry' would go droning on and on and on. Jim only attended Sunday School to please his mother who held to some curious notions. Sunday School was where the children of nice, respectable parents spent their Sunday afternoons. This custom allowed such parents a bit of a breather, safe in the knowledge that their offspring would be out of possible mischief for an hour or two. And a bit of preaching/teaching would do them no harm and might even do them a mite of good.

Jim looked up, not, by a long chalk, for the first time, at the framed cheap print of the flaxen haired and bearded young man who, with sad eyes and faintly melancholy expression, gazed down from the wall of Harry Martin's small classroom. The figure wore what appeared to be a flowing and loosely draped white nightshirt. Jim could not establish, to his own satisfaction, any clear convincing way of relating to this depiction of Christ.

Nor did Biblical stories greatly impress him. With the moral messages of one or two he positively disagreed, though he kept his thoughts to himself.

The parable of the Prodigal Son was a case in point. Being a fairly dutiful stay at home himself, Jim rather sided with the elder son who complained when the fatted calf was slaughtered for the returning Prodigal. The elder son, unlike the younger, had not consorted with harlots – and neither had Jim. And anyway, who was to say that the younger son was genuine in his contrition? The great love and ready forgiveness extended by a parent were fine in themselves. But surely, love of any kind could become excessive? Otherwise words like 'doting' and 'uxorious' would not have been coined?

And besides, where was the mother, granny too for that matter, in all this moralising about the prodigal son? As far as Jim's experience went, it was his Mother and the mothers of friends and cousins who held families together and provided the prime moral guidance.

Certainly, it was the one grandmother he had known who had possessed the strength of character and conscience to bring up a family of seven children on a labourer's wage and to remain kind, understanding, encouraging – to seventeen grandchildren. This gem of a woman, content, not bitter with her lot, died at seventy, physically worn out.

It would be to Gran's old home that Jim would be going for tea after Sunday School. Those great sports of uncles – Harold and Les would be there, and his mom (for she would prepare the meal) – but not his dad. Wilf, true to his Victorian values, insisted on having his own meals in his own home. Such stubborn insistence often meant Jim or his Mom scooting about with cloth covered plates of food in a wicker basket.

Just as he had hoped – tinned salmon it was for tea – delicious when drenched in vinegar. Cling peaches, topped with a blob of condensed milk to follow – super delicious. And then, with washing up out of the way – sin exquisite, Sunday evenings games of cards – Rummy, Pontoon, Newmarket – with matches for stakes: 'England's Glory', naturally.

Occasionally the wind-up, table top gramophone was brought in to tinny use and from a pitted and worn piece of shellac would issue the crackling, hissing music and words of:

"Horsey keep your tail up

Keep the sun out of my eyes..."

Jim's Mother would giggle like a schoolgirl as she listened to the thin, reedy voice of the singer. Jim permitted himself a smirk and glanced in the direction of the black horsehair sofa that brooded evilly beneath the window of the tiny, overcrowded dining/living room with its cast iron range and bulky, highly polished sideboard. Jim glowered in the direction of the sofa. His flesh had healed but the emotional scars remained. For it was on this sinister inquisitional piece of furniture that he had many a time sat, as a small boy in shorts, squashed between sombrely dressed stout ladies, of melancholy disposition. Trapped as he was, the coarse, prickly horsehair (beloved of religious penitents and the hairshirt brigade) stabbed maliciously at his tender flesh.

Even worse, the black crones nodded in agreeably mournful unison as they openly wondered whether 'Sal will be able to rear him,' that small, pale faced boy silenced somewhere among the thickly corseted matrons. Inwardly Jim raged, silently vowing that 'he'd show 'em' some day.

"Let's change the record shall we?"

Harold rapidly wound up the gramophone and set another favourite record – a Jack Hylton – on the turntable.

"The flies crawled up the window,

That's all they had to do,

They went up by the thousand,

And came down two by two..."

"Remind me James, to put a fly paper on the next shopping list. It won't add much weight to what you have to carry from the Co-op."

"OK Ma, my biceps will just about be up to it."

"And don't call me 'Ma'. You know I don't like it!"

"OK M--om."

Jim could well believe that in summertime especially, there'd be far more bluebottles in his new home than in his old. Hell!

"Right our kid, let's have something a bit more romantic now."

Harold deferred good naturedly to his sister who began to smile in a slightly dreamy manner as another reedy tenor voice entered the cluttered but warm and cosy mini casino at the back of the boot repairer's workshop, (knock three times and ask for Cherry Blossom).

"Marta rambling rose of the wild wood,

Marta with your fragrance divine,

Rosebud of the days of my childhood ..."

The record screeched to an end.

"That's quite enough of "Marta let me take off your garter." Let's have a game of pontoon."

Uncle Les picked up a pack of well used playing cards and dextrously flicked a hand to each of the four players.

Quick though Les was, Jim had already lapsed into a daydream. Marta was certainly an uncommon name. Come to think of it, were there many songs with girls' names for titles? Well, there was 'Barbara Allen', but that tune didn't make your feet tap. What about dance tunes then? Well, there was 'Amy, wonderful Amy' – in praise of the great flier Amy Johnson – 'Me and Jane in a plane'. 'When I met Connie in the Cornfield' – now that seemed more like it and; a piercing whistle split the air – then, "Wake up Junior, buy one or twist?"

A lively voice put paid to 'Junior's' reverie.

Jimmy turned his head to meet the blue, twinkling eyes and broad grin of sporty Les, a champ at snooker, darts, cards (especially crib), crown green bowls, a man highly popular at the local Workingmen's Club, and among his fellow factory floor workers. Come to think of it, he did bear some resemblance to Fred Astaire – straight fair hair, a lantern jaw, a slim, quick man of lithe movements.

"Twist."

"Bust."

With a good-natured jest about the deficiencies of a grammar school education, Les swept Jimmy's stake into the banker's steadily growing pile of matches.

"What about you our kid? Twist or buy one?"

Harold, the elder brother pondered, hesitated, pithered.

"Come on Christmas, I've got a bird to see later."

He usually had. Lucky so and so.

Harold sniggered and looked at his four cards – yet again – wondering whether he dare risk going for a five card trick. Only the top edges of the backs of his cards could be seen by the other players. Harold wasn't being cagey and he didn't much care whether he won or lost. The seeming excess concealment was due simply to his being the owner of massive hands with thick muscular fingers. A physically strong man, and a gentle man was Harold – the readily acknowledged 'tops' among the family gardeners and winner of many prizes at flower shows small and large.

"Buy one."

Les slid a card, face down, across the worn, smooth cloth that covered the gate-legged table – a highly practical table for a small room.

"Bust."

"Thought so."

Les whistled a snatch from 'We're in the money' as he scooped up more matches.

Sitting to one side of the players, Grandad, an 'ancient' of about seventy five, took no part in these high spirited card games but would watch with interest for some of the time. For the most part, the banter passed him by as he was quite hard of hearing and other people did seem to mumble so these days. At intervals, he would darken his deep gingery moustache by carefully sipping hot tea from a large saucer. This he would periodically re-fill with a rock steady, well practised hand, from a large breakfast cup. No man enjoyed his tea more.

With the tea sipping ritual finished, another ritual began. With unstudied deliberation, the old man opened his clasp knife and slowly cut off a chunk of black twist tobacco to stuff and light in his much loved pipe. Soon the card players were set to spluttering but the game went on. So did the puffing out, in great contentment, of foul smelling smoke. Mild protests, especially from his daughter, seemed only to strengthen the old man's 'Deaf Dicky' defences.

Having bankrupted, yet again, his sister, his brother and his nephew, Les issued another brisk challenge.

"Fancy a game of darts Junior before we get as smoked as kippers? There's just time for a game of 301 before I meet my bird. Anyway, I know she'll wait even if I am a bit late."

Jimmy hung the dartboard from the curtain pole (fixed above a door frame) which held in place a thick, extensively and luridly patched, blanket type curtain reaching to the floor. Behind that draught semi-excluder lay, to the left, the cellar steps, to the right, the pantry alcove and straight ahead the door (locked from the far side) to the cobblers in what, in palmier days, would have been the parlour. (But the cobbler helped with the rent.)

Behind that patchwork curtain also lay part of Jim's history – his botched attempts (screened from his listening mother) to recite, word for word, poems, and extracts from the Bible he had been required to learn as homework.

"And there shall come forth a rod out of the stem of Jesse..." never made a lot of sense to Jim so his attention wandered, to plagues of boils for instance, accompanied by the wish that such or similar punishment, frogs perhaps, could be visited upon those who inflicted such misery upon growing schoolboys.

'London Snow' by Robert Bridges he greatly enjoyed. The poem was so wonderfully evocative and so skilfully composed;

"...deadening, muffling, stifling its murmurs failing,
Lazily and incessantly floating down, and down..."

But crikey, those lines were so dashed difficult to memorise and even more difficult to recite – word perfect. What a misery that day at school when he was picked to stand up and recite. More lines as an impot for failure.

"Snap out of it dreamer. Ready?"

"OK"

"Middle for diddle?"

"OK"

Les's arrow sped straight to the bull. Jimmy's landed close to double 17 and – fell out.

By adopting a sideways stance, it was just possible to stand with reasonable comfort between the table and the ruddy, highly burnished sideboard; the only decent stick of furniture in the whole house, a gift from some toffs' household where Jim's grandmother had been in service back in the early 1880s.

301 soon became 0 for Les. Another whitewash for Jim who had failed to get a starting double.

Les, whistling jauntily, headed, with sprightly step, for romance. Jimmy drew a hard wooden chair closer to the fire. His Grandad, similarly seated, pored over the *News of the World*. Grandson watched Grandad with interest, for 'Junior' knew that 'Senior' would be sure to miss the spicy bits about some clergyman or other – but not for any puritanical beliefs the old man might have held.

No, Grandad was not a churchgoing man. Sunday mornings, working on the plot, followed by a pint in the adjacent Workingmen's Club, followed by the best dinner of the week. Daughter Sal saw to that. The plot grown veggies were a great help too. Sunday afternoons – bed – followed by the best tea of the week, followed (at a decent interval), by a couple of hours, and a couple of drinks, back at the Club.

The tired old eyes scanned each page of the Sunday paper with slow painstaking care. Years ago Jim had spotted that his Grandad seemed to pay particular and repeated attention to the photographs and illustrations of the *Daily Mirror*, or any paper for that matter. There lay the clue. His Grandad could neither read nor write but protected his self-esteem by apparent careful scrutiny of the printed word.

And here *he* was, his grandson, a grammar bug to boot, learning about queer things such as algebra (which would grow no potatoes at all, let alone King Edwards on any allotment, for any Sunday dinner) and, blast! he had just remembered that he still hadn't mastered those theorems for 'Pip', a softly spoken but authoritative and burly Maths teacher.

Ah well, perhaps he'd get up earlier tomorrow morning and have another stab at his homework. But, of course, he didn't.

Chapter Three
"Shining Morning Face"

"Are you sure you've got a clean handkerchief?"

"Yes Ma – er, sorry, Mom."

"Cheese and tomato be all right?"

"Fine."

"Not getting tired of them?"

Sal was making up Jimmy's customary sandwiches. He couldn't abide school dinners.

"No, but I wouldn't mind a marmalade sandwich – and a piece of your coconut cake as well."

With this far more toothsome balance of rations, Jim set off on his mile long walk to Handsworth Grammar School – the boys only grammar in Grove Lane.

The greater part of his trek wound through Handsworth Park which he entered by the massive, curlicued, wrought iron gates in Hamstead Road. One of Birmingham's most prestigious open spaces, site of the city's annual flower show, and scouts' rallies; Handsworth Park was bisected by a railway running through cuttings and along an embankment. Kicking the occasional pebble in best Pongo Waring (Villa's former centre forward) style, Jim walked over the main railway bridge and headed across open grassland, for the smaller of the Grove Lane exits.

In Grove Lane he met up with 'Lofty' Hill, a rangy bespectacled fellow fifth former. Jim stretched his short, stocky legs to keep in step with his long legged classmate.

"By the way, Lofty, I've got some fag card swaps. Take a gander at these."

The boys stopped.

Jim fished in his battered leather satchel and handed over a small shoal of some sixty odd brightly coloured cards, mostly depicting film stars and sports personalities. Lofty carefully sorted through the haul looking for numbers to help complete sets.

"I could do with these."

Lofty held out for inspection a clutch of Wills' 'Association Footballers', and, with a whistle of appreciation, some Players 'Film Stars – Second Series': sparkling Ginger Rogers, sultry Dolores Del Rio and that doughty dame for all seasons and reasons, Mae West.

"She's a lot too old for you."

"Who is?"

"Mae West."

"Hot stuff though."

"So I've been told."

"Pity you haven't got one of Pongo."

At the mention of that illustrious name both boys spontaneously joined in a *sotto voce* chant;

"Pongo Waring was so daring,
He tried to score a goal,
He missed his kick,
And split his knicks,
And showed his dirty – umpah, umpah, stick it up your jumpah."

"Getting back to Mae West, have you heard the one about her being like a wireless set?"

Jim was tempted to say 'yes' so as to avoid the slight embarrassment he usually felt at listening to dirty jokes. But throughout his young life his mother had repeatedly dinned into him the crucial importance, to right and proper conduct, of being truthful. So he said 'no', thereby keeping his integrity intact while hoping that he might, by listening, be both amused and also add to his meagre store of knowledge about one of life's great mysteries – the making of life itself.

"Well, Mae West said, 'You first have to get tuned in so twiddle the dials a while.'" Lofty simulated such sorcery with his hands close to his chest. "And the boyfriend said, 'Well I'm not getting much of a reception yet.' And Mae West said, 'Well, just wait big boy 'til you get plugged in.'"

Jimmy laughed; "it" did sound rather more fun than messing about with a Wheatstone Bridge in the Physics Lab!

Lofty returned to the morally safer ground of fag card inspection. "Ta, I don't want these though. And a few of them are stuck together."

That was the trouble with the new sticky back issues, designed to be placed permanently in their appropriate albums, "ask your tobacconist for the attractive album (price one penny) specially prepared to hold the complete series." The least little spot of moisture, – from sweaty football socks for instance, and the damage was done.

"I'll bring my swaps on Friday."

"Right ho – Lofty – 'Motor Cars 2nd Series' if you've got any."

"OK, I think I've got a few."

Fag card collecting depended entirely on smoking habits. Jim himself was no boy for a crafty drag in the park shrubbery – not for any moralistic reasons but simply because he cherished athletic ambitions, and believed that as a non-smoker, he would prove to be a better runner.

Besides, he was assured a steady if uneven buckshee supply of cards from relatives who gasped and wheezed – and from the gutters where fag packets, empty of fags but still containing a card, were commonly tossed aside. So with the aid of fellow swappers, Jim was now close to completing his latest target of Players 'Motor Cars – Second Series', in its 1d album. Completion would enable him to indulge his fancy of one day driving a Morgan "4-4" or, at a pinch, zipping around in an Aston Martin 2 Litre Speed Model.

The boys entered the school yard and made for the lavs in the far corner. It was a cold, raw day.

"By the way Lofty, are you entering for the cross country race this year?"

"Sure thing."

"Tell you what, let's train together in Perry Playing Fields on Saturday."

"OK What time?"

"Half past two by the changing rooms? Time to let your suet pud go down."

"OK I'll be there."

The bell rang for assembly and some six hundred boys brought their hubbub from outdoors into the hall. Chattering and sniggering soon died away as the relatively new, rosy cheeked headmaster, fizzing with energy and combative Christian zeal, strode briskly onto the stage.

Jim didn't quite know what to make of 'Holy Joe', the Reverend H. R. Gordon. That he was a strict disciplinarian had been made painfully plain. But this formidable divine held some very curious views on sports and sporting occasions. Really what *was* the point of trying to stop his charges, at inter-school sports days, from lustily bellowing their war cries;

"Witchabella, witchabella, ra, ra, ra...Attaboy, attaboy, bulldog, bulldog – H a n d s w o r t h."

Jim, now standing in a line of fifth formers wasn't quite sure whether to sing in an uncertain baritone, or gruff bass, another of the Head's 'uplifting' musical innovations.

"On sure foundations,
Build we God's new nations..."

Suddenly, a small hard object was pressed into his left hand by Dandy Sandy standing next to him. It felt like a couple of squares of block chocolate wrapped in tin foil. Jim took a discreet peep and peeled back a corner of the tin foil. Yes, it was chocolate, but a rather special brand, too rich for his taste – Ex-Lax. Jim grinned and quickly passed this aid to the irregular to his right.

"Bridges from man to man,
The whole wide world to span..."

Perhaps the school itself in recent years had needed a good dose of salts, and a gingering up, from new vigorous leadership. Certainly, within a short space of time, the new head had brought about academic changes which meant that Jim in his fourth year, was, with others, in the fifth form – 5C in fact. Confusing to those not in the know. What Jim did realise was that he, along with his classmates (and the Latin learning bugs of 5A) would have to take the 'Matric' this year instead of next – a break with the five year study tradition. What a rotten swizz!

Quite apart from seeking to cope with that fiendish torment called Algebra, it had been hard enough coming to terms with a grammar bug education at a school which, even an eleven year old dimwit in short trousers could recognise was undergoing turbulent change.

As a timid junior in 1C and then Remove C, Jim had initially blundered about in a fog of uncertainty, only partially succeeding in matching a curious muddle of expectations to a volatile reality.

Handsworth Grammar had turned out to be so very different from Greyfriars of *The Magnet*. No, 'I say you fellows', Bunter yaroohing; no Harry Wharton type of gang. Some teachers spoke so oddly, very oddly in fact of 'grarse', and 'carstle'; a baffling new language in itself. The Rev. H.R. clamped down on unruly behaviour and, as Jim clearly remembered, he had once banned games of football in the yard. Next day, long lines of senior boys had signalled defiance by skipping outside the head's study while others feigned knitting motions, with balls of wool strewn about. Stormy days. But as boys left to become old boys, and new fags enrolled, Jim noticed that calmer behaviour standards began to gain ground.

However, Jim's own behaviour on that Ex-Lax Monday still left room for marked improvement.

"Sit up straight Norton!"

"Stop slouching Norton!"

Six times during the lesson did an exasperated 'Pip' attempt to get Jim to straighten his backbone and to straighten out his geometric thoughts.

"Detention for you my lad."

Jim assumed a suitably sullen expression but he didn't appeal against the sentence, accepting that he had been 'asking for it.'

Like his Dad repeatedly affirmed from that shabby old chair; "fair play's a jewel."

*

Grudgingly at first and then more readily, Jim adapted to his shabby new home. He drew strength from one of his mom's favourite sayings, 'wisdom' which seemed to enjoy universal unquestioning acceptance among relatives, friends, neighbours and acquaintances: 'What can't be cured must be endured.'

And so, slowly, he began to adjust to the dump, even being prepared to pull his weight in household chores in a genial and not resentful manner.

"Now that you're not playing football tomorrow, I'd like you to help me with a little job I've got."

"Right Ma."

"And don't call me Ma."

"Right Mother dear – what is this mighty task?"

"Don't be sarky."

"Right ho, what is it you want me to do then?"

"Well this room badly needs re-decorating and -"

"I'll say it does."

"Don't interrupt dear."

"Sorry."

"Well, as I was about to say, Bill has offered to do the paper hanging - and I've bought the wallpaper - six rolls of it. But it needs trimming. So that's where you come in." And that was how, on a wet Saturday afternoon with the football pitch water-logged, that young Jim came to be sitting in Ma's armchair, his outstretched legs slightly bent, his feet about 18" apart. Across his insteps rested a roll of wallpaper. With his left hand he pulled the loose end of the roll towards him, picked up the scissors in his right hand and began to cut away the half inch or so of 'waste' on the right hand side of the roll.

"Don't rush it dear, and don't go drifting off into one of your daydreams! You need to concentrate to get a straight edge."

"Right ho, Ma."

Sal thought it best not to rebuke her son now that he had obviously made a good start. She took up her knitting - a jumper for herself. The pattern was intricate. Neither handiworker spoke for a while, then:

"Do you think there'll be another war Mom?"

Jim's Mother, caught unawares, played for time:

"Why on earth do you ask such a question?"

"Oh, it's just that some of us were talking about it at school and wondering whether we'd join the army, navy or airforce. I fancy the navy myself."

"Well, I'd rather you didn't talk about such matters. It's all too horrible to think about, it really is."

"OK" The snipping resumed.

"There you are then, six rolls finished."

"Well done, and thank you. You've done your old mom a real good turn. Now before you get ready to go out monkey running with young Ken, there's one more little job you can do for me."

"Oh heck - what's that?"

"Just hold this skein of wool for me while I roll it into a ball."

An easy enough job that, but boring. Some concentration was still needed to ensure that the tension in the skein was just right, and that

the light movement of the hands was sufficiently rhythmic to allow the thread of wool to be wound round the growing ball at the best possible speed. Jim thought a song might help;
"'There was a young lady of Ealing
Who walked upside down on the ceiling,
She fell on her neck
And she shouted "by heck",
It's a very peculiar feeling.

That was a cute little rhyme
Sing us another one do.

There was a young fellow of Cosham
Who took out his false teeth to wash 'em -'"
"That's quite enough of that, thank you."
"But it's sung on the wireless and Bill knows some really funny verses so he tells me."
"I don't doubt it, but he won't be singing them here if I have anything to do with it. So pipe down young man."
Jim tried another tack, another novelty number.
"'Oh you can't do that there 'ere,
Oh you can't do that there 'ere,
Anywhere else you can do that there,
But you can't do that there 'ere.'"
Sal took a mock swing with her arm at her son's head.
Jim ducked - and assumed his George Formby voice,
"Yah - never touched me!"
Yes, things were looking up;
"'No matter what they say
Things are getting better, better, better every day.'"

*

And so, loathing for the dump slowly turned into tolerance and easy familiarity, almost a kind of exasperated affection. But he never became fully reconciled to the new environment. He often raged, inwardly, at the lack of a bathroom and of somewhere quiet and warm in which to study.

Deep down, having lived the first fourteen years of his life near a hill top, he chafed at the gloomy, restrictive valley perspective of this meaner, grubbier house.

Still, he had to admit that life was brightening just a little. He began to receive fewer impots. Thanks to Lofty, he completed his Motor Cars – second series set. And better times still were nearing – the school cross country race – and his birthday. He entertained hopes about the race that he would only express in his diary.

His race training programme was perhaps a touch idiosyncratic. Jim drew inspiration for the manly ordeal in two main ways – by intently studying yellowing newspaper cuttings carefully folded in his diary, and by re-reading, with undiminished pleasure about Jimmy Lester.

The cuttings featured the achievements of a young British solicitor who the year before had broken the world record for the mile in 4 minutes 6.4 seconds – a nation's hero, Sidney Wooderson.

And Jimmy Lester? A fictional hero from Warnes *Pleasure Book for Boys*, a present from the aunt who had borne, and raised, nine children – a marvellous exemplar of stamina. Jimmy had been chosen as second string in a team of four to represent his school against a rival school in a cross country race, forever known as 'The Big Run'. Just before the start, Jimmy was instructed to set a sufficiently fast pace to break the crack but metronomic runner of the opposing team: in short, to sacrifice his own chance of a place – for the good of the school. Jimmy duly broke the crack and, in a desperate finish, broke the tape to tumultuous cheering. A great tale of fidelity, pluck and deserved triumph.

As for the physical aspects of the training, let the athlete's own diary attest to the rigour involved.

23 February. "Did a quarter hr running in back kitchen. Training for cross country."

Clearly this training tip was not taken from a recognised coaching manual. Sheer improvisation really. His mother wouldn't allow him to run in the pouring rain – so running on the spot it had to be. On a red quarry tiled floor he ran with some vigour and more care, so as not to collide with the gas stove or the heavy cast iron mangle opposite. Actually, he thought it quite fun to 'bounce' against the coarse, heavy and knobbled roller towel hanging from the door that led to the blue bricked backyard. The remainder of the kitchen was fully taken up by the sink, much used wash boiler, an unused fireplace, a cupboard and a wooden 'safe', the workingman's 'fridge', which, with its metal mesh door, briefly kept meat, cheese and marge – above the rancid level – and free of flies.

Steadily, the training programme became more venturesome; running round the school's playing fields in Handsworth Wood, around Perry Hall Playing Fields, usually with Lofty, sometimes with Doug Baker, now living in a posh semi in Great Barr. The day came, 16th March, and Jim came fifth having been "second equal till last quarter of mile", a form of self consolation. Not too bad though.

By now Jim was making regular entries in his Letts Schoolboy's Diary, a Christmas present from his Dad, terse entries admittedly but eminently to the point.

"Library tickets ready tomorrow. Nice dame behind counter."

"Dad's birthday. Gave him 6d."

Nothing fancy mark you. Nothing wrapped. After he had handed over the gift Jim realised that such 'generosity' represented one penny per decade. Still, a silvery tanner could buy his Dad a good seat at the pictures, or a quarter of Rowntrees' gums or a packet of Craven A cigarettes, "the smoothest smoke of all".

Such calculations prompted Jim to check his diary for financial facts. Under the New Year's resolution impulse, he had recorded details of the first couple of months pocket money. The weekly average turned out to be ninepence, mostly provided by those two steady, wage earning uncles, Les and Harold, with their elder brother Sam, running them a close third. With 9d Jim knew he could have bought two Dinky toys – say a mechanical horse (a three wheeler tug type vehicle much in vogue in railway yards) priced 6d and a traffic light signal 3d. These might have been worth while buying, had he owned a model railway, but he didn't. Case closed.

Still, there was never any lack of competing claims on the 9d. Just take the unofficial school tuck shop for a start. Here, the lusciously buxom, back chatting Gwen tipped with dextrous wrist, and unstinting display of pink and white cleavage, coconut chips (in matching pink and white) into cone shaped paper bags. It was a highly popular tuckshop. In summer, the cleavage deepened and speculation ran at near fever pitch as to how much clothing Gwen was wearing under that flowered overall. Whew! It made the senses reel when the bosomy siren mixed a scoop of ice cream into the ginger beer. Could she be an English Mae West in waiting?

But back to the nine pence. Could such opulence be spread to cover magazines and comics, an occasional tram-fare into 'town', the city centre? What would happen if a girlfriend ever came along? Subs from his mom, un-entered in the diary accounts, would not, could not, be doubled, that was a certainty. But as yet, that "girls are expensive you know" threat seemed remote. Or did it?

*

"Do you think Eden was right to resign?"

Ken frowned; a rare event.

"I dunno – I suppose Musso's getting pretty pushy."

"And not just Musso. Hitler's getting too big for his jackboots as well. Expect there'll be a big bust up one of these days."

"Well, never mind that now. Are you coming with me to the Guild on Thursday?"

"Maybe."

"There'll be some new bits of fluff there."

"Really."

Ken would know wouldn't he? He'd probably planned the whole business. The son of Quaker parents, he attended a Friends' Meeting House for Sunday service and the Guild, in effect a Youth Club, was organised by that church. On the Sunday Ken had doubtless encouraged two promising gigglers to turn up for the debate the following Thursday, when he promised that his pal would be there to make up a foursome.

From autumn to spring the Guild conducted a weekly programme of talks, debates, socials, Beetle Drives, and, on occasional Saturdays, a dance. Situated in Farm Street, among the meaner streets of Hockley, where real poverty, and not just hard times existed – the Guild did fine work with youngsters from all backgrounds.

Jimmy's table tennis skills improved. So did his self-confidence as he made growing contributions to the debates. When sufficiently captivated by some sorceress, he had been known to shuffle his size 8s in movements that bore an indifferent resemblance to a St. Bernard's waltz.

But what a motion for that particular Thursday evening debate! A real corker for its day!

That "chivalry is an insult to women and a nuisance to men".

Such a wildly heretical motion was predictably lost – and so the doors from the hall were still opened by the lads for the lasses to pass through.

As to the bits of stuff, Ken had "got it bad for Margery now", whereas the far less ardent Jimmy who had sat next to Elsie, evaluated her (Elsie that is) as "not bad". Such a judgement was based not on moral standards but overall appearance and impression created.

Jim was now fifteen years and two days old. On his birthday, 5th April, the 'celebrations' had been somewhat mixed in character. His presents totalled six shillings and sixpence; his cards – seven; and examinations sat – two; "Physics not too bad, German pretty rotten". He borrowed a P.G.Wodehouse title from the public library, 'Right Ho, Jeeves', and finished the day by joining Ken at his home where their mouth-organ duets 'entertained' an indulgent audience. Ken lived with his doting widowed mother and her spinster sister.

Jim considered himself to be 'not too bad' an harmonica player. At least the neighbours had never hammered on the wall in protest. He persevered valiantly with the only bit of musical talent (paper and comb, and kazoo apart) he possessed; eventually listing one hundred and thirty tunes he could play in reasonably recognisable fashion. Tunes he could hum in his head, but with forgotten titles, featured in this repertoire alongside such old standards as 'Bye Bye Blackbird,' and the much later 'September in the Rain'. What a magnificent (1937) version by the band of Joe Loss, vocal Chick Henderson. Just great!

Although April 5th 1923 was self-evidently of some importance to James and his parents, there was nothing to suggest that it was a particularly auspicious day for mankind in general. True, the perceptive *Birmingham Mail* reported the death of an interesting old gaffer, one Isaac Lamb, aged 106 who, apparently, had smoked and chewed tobacco since he was 11. Such news must have cheered those who hacked, gasped and wheezed while enjoying their 'coffin nails.'

On seeing that report, some years later, Jim fell to wondering if Isaac had been a fag card collector. If so, what mountains of cards the old man must have collected! And all before the days of the new fangled, not totally to be trusted, sticky backs. Mountains – simply mountains.

Jim thought back to what his mom had told him about his birth at No. 96. Eminently highly practical housewife though she was, Sal cherished her dreams. She claimed partly to believe what she maintained the midwife had told her, 'One day your son will be a famous Cross Channel swimmer – you mark my words.'

The 'justification' for such a bold prediction rested on one simple fact. On each foot, two of Jimmy's toes were partly joined. This 'oddity' would surely make for superb swimming capabilities. Jim would hum to himself, 'Be kind to your web-footed friends, for a duck may be somebody's mother.' Such nonsense, the whole notion.

In April 1938, with exhausting effort, he could just about manage a length at the public baths. But cherish your dreams Mom.

Still, the date of April 5th did bring a touch of good fortune to both sides of the family – well, to those who had backed a horse of that name in 1932, when "April 5th" galloped home the Derby winner. Starting price, 100-6.

Jim now began to wonder whether he would also prove to be a winner at the school sports to take place on Saturday, 14th May. Training, outside the kitchen, began.

Chapter Four
Mostly Playtime

Perry Barr's bustling shopping centre, still identified by the "old 'uns" as "the village", boasted two picture houses. The Birchfields, ("The Birchies" to the "young 'uns") a small, brick built, homely little cinema, was far too clean and well kept to be labelled a flea pit. It stood a cosy, unpretentious near neighbour of that much larger and quite splendid white oriental palace – the first Odeon to be built in the country.

Now he was fifteen, and as a break from reluctantly trailing along with Ken on various monkey runs (spring was back with the parks again available for dating games), Jimmy became a regular picture goer. Occasional nearby 'supporting features' formed an added attraction; for example, a display outside a cinema, of searchlights by units of the Territorial Army. The notion that Britain should strengthen its defences seemed to be gaining ground. So was the opinion that Britons themselves ought to be a jolly sight fitter.

Jim chortled at the antics of gormless, but wily, George Formby in *Keep Fit*.

"Keep fit, take exercise …Whatever you do, keep fit," sang toothy George to his ukulele plucking.

Catching the mood of the day, Jim set about collecting a new series of cigarette cards. *Keep Fit* was well illustrated, depicting twenty-five 'Exercises for Women' and twenty-five 'Exercises for Men'. Ladies first, and equal shares; no-one could be fairer than that.

The male demonstrator was no muscle bound Charles Atlas and the lady counterpart no skinny bird, appearing lissom but curvaceous in best Health and Beauty style, black shorts and short sleeved white blouse.

Jim audaciously wondered (silently, of course) how Saucy Sue might look in such a sporty outfit. Sue and Joan had been chatted up

– or rather Ken had done the chatting, in Handsworth Park – by the bandstand. On the briefest of acquaintances, Jim evaluated Sue as "very fast", as she nudged him now and then in the side with her elbow, and made one or two racy innuendoes; at least he thought that's perhaps what they were. *"Date for Friday same place."*

No luck – the girls didn't show. Saucy Sue had probably decided that one meeting with that pair was quite enough, thank you, 'God's gift to girls' and that slow-witted kid with the goofy tooth! So often did Jim long for that twisted upper front tooth to be miraculously straightened.

Still, Jim wasn't greatly disappointed at being stood up, for all things considered, he was feeling "pretty rotten". His stubborn, barking cough had failed to respond to the hitherto much trusted raspberry vinegar treatment: his legs felt weak and rubbery: the borrowed running spikes from the school's battered stock badly needed repairing: he lost a day from school (only the second in four years) because of an itchy rash which, in the doctor's opinion, was due to food poisoning: "fish we had for dinner." So, one way and another, Sports Day found him a touch ill prepared for possible athletic fame.

Contrary then to general expectations, Jim did not appear in the first three home in either the 100 or 220 yard sprints of the Intermediate Boys' Events. 'Verily and forsooth', as erudite fifth formers were wont to proclaim, this was not the best of days for dreamy young Jim. And the fates remained relentlessly hostile. "Had piece taken out of my heel by bench. Kids mucking about. Had 9d pinched." Lackaday.

Fortunately, the selectors were sufficiently enlightened not to judge runners solely on their Sports Day performances. Jim was picked to run for the Intermediate relay team at the city's inter-school sports – "I ran OK." He wasn't given to fulsome self praise – even in a diary.

And now a hurdle was nearing, the clearing of which, really mattered – the School Certificate examination. Far brighter prospects were thought to await those who gained their 'Matric' than those who didn't. On 30th May Jimmy started swotting. On 1st June he decided to relax a little and went to the pictures, to the Perry Barr Odeon on his own – but not for long. "Polly Parsons came and sat by me. Molly and new pal came and first sat behind and then in front of us."

What was going on? he wondered. Was Polly interested in what her friends might do when she came to join him? Had they egged Polly on to make this rather forward, for a young lady, move? Did they then move to signal to Polly that they were not going to spy? Or was it an opportunity to turn in their seats to catch Polly and Jimmy holding hands, or simply to take a closer look at the boy Polly had brazenly decided to join?

Jim wondered and wondered. He knew in a general sense that girls could be so devious, but it was so darned difficult to tell on any particular occasion what they were really up to. Snigger, snigger; giggle, giggle; whisper, whisper; all that you could be sure of but little else.

Take the Sunday School outing for instance, to Yarningale Common. In the larking about on the back seat of the coach, the elder of two sisters had slapped James smartly across the face for keeping her coat belt. Was Betty's annoyance genuine, feigned or simply what was expected of a young lady who had been too much teased? Oh heck, questions questions. More followed.

*

"...imagine that you have been avoiding the company of one of your greatest friends under the impression that he (or she) has done you an injury. Write a letter of apology (about 100 words) on discovering that you have been mistaken."

"Write a composition in French," (150-200 words), "on...
    (b) Un vieil âne raconte son histoire."
(Jim grinned and thought of "good old Pop.")

" ...ii) Divide £ 15 13s 4½d by 23, expressing your result as a decimal of £1 correct to two decimal places."

On that particular day, searching questions were also being asked of English bowlers for they had been hammered by Don Bradman who scored 100 in seventy-three minutes at Old Trafford. A great side that – from Australia. O'Reilly, for one, was back again;
    "If you're the O'Reilly
    They speak of so highly,

Then gorblimey O'Reilly,
You don't half bowl well."
Weekly Illustrated, June 11, 1938 – price 2d – put the matter just slightly differently: "The Bowler England Most Fear."

Soon followed the gaping, lacklustre post examination period of yawning boredom, flicking ink pellets with the aid of a ruler, playing battleships and hangman – and more yawning boredom, punctuated by bursts of organised energy designed to entertain – a concert, plays and PT contests.

Then, for the first time that he could remember, Jim experienced a tingling sensation running up and down his spine; almost like a soft but very rapid playing of a xylophone, with but a single note.

At the school's Music Competition a radical, pioneering boy named Linton broke with the light classical and classical tradition of such occasions, by playing, not only the rather *infra dig* saxophone, but Hoagy Carmichael's 'Stardust' into the bargain, to wildly enthusiastic applause.

Excerpts from *Julius Caesar* did not receive the same rapturous reception, but many more laughs than were warranted by Shakespeare's script. No fault of Jim's – he was hardly in the limelight, doubling simply as a servant and "Second citizen."

He readily acknowledged that he had no acting ability or interest, and still occasionally wondered why he had been chosen to play the role of Nelson in an historical sketch at Junior School. Perhaps he had looked sufficiently waif like at the time to represent Britain's most illustrious sailor in the deathbed scene. Years of eating bread and scrape, with sugar sometimes sprinkled over the doorsteps, lettuce, condensed milk may have contributed to Jim's wan appearance.

Anyway, there he was in about 1931 being tenderly lowered to the *Victory's* deck by sorrowing shipmates. Lying on his back, Jim looked up at the ring of deeply concerned faces bent over him. Suddenly, he remembered something his teasing sister May had once told him as being 'real history that is'.

"Kiss me Hardy," murmured the fast fading admiral.

For a split second the faces of his crew above him seemed stupefied. Then peal after peal of clear laughter rang out – and the teacher joined in. A double mortification for Jim that day. But he had since wondered whether Captain Hardy was being played by a pretty girl – Mary Park perhaps or Helen Bright? Sadly, he couldn't remember.

Make-believe seemed to be very much in the air during the summer of 1938. Take some of the magazine adverts for instance. By using a particular threepenny tablet of soap, a lady could have a "schoolgirl complexion all over." Well, it was worth thinking about, Jim supposed, "all over" mark you. At the other end of the rainbow imagination – "Noxacorn ... dries up calluses and corns, root and all . . . 1/6 bottle saves untold misery." Whew! A bit steep that and who would want to save misery? Ho! Ho!

Weekly Illustrated, under the heading "G.B.S. puts Hitler and Mussolini on the Stage", gave an account of a "political harlequinade" written by George Bernard Shaw: "now in his eighty-third year", and presented at the Malvern Festival. "...thus Shaw shows the League [of Nations] to be the farce that it has become, flays dictators – and leaves you to think out for yourself what is to be the answer." 'Cor! A tall order,' thought Jim.

In mid-July, Birmingham itself took to the stage, presenting a week long pageant in Aston Park to celebrate its centenary as a city. Each evening, episodes from Birmingham's history were enacted by ordinary people – the 'Priestly Riots', for instance, a citizens' revolt against the radical ideas of the turbulent priest scientist.

Different districts of Birmingham undertook responsibility for the presentation of particular historical aspects. Edg-bar-ston (a really, really posh suburb) certainly possessed the brass, surface refinement and correct plummy accents to portray the fripperies and fopperies of the Restoration.

Gladys Cooper, famed beauty and much photographed actress of the Edwardian era, came to christen one of the mock dinosaurs on display. For the life of him, Jim couldn't fathom why his factory hand Uncle Harold should want to caper and holler about, clad in sacking, making out he was Gus Grit an ancient Brit. Had the photos in the paper of 'glorious Glad' fired him up?

'It was a pretty pricey pageant,' Jim thought, the cheapest reserved seat being 2/4d, doubled to 4/8d – the day the Royals, the Duke and Duchess of Gloucester, came to watch.

The pageant could keep its dinosaurs. Ken and Jim had far prettier game to pursue, through the grasslands, savannahs and prairies of Handsworth Park, Perry Hall Playing Fields and Perry Park.

Sometimes Jim strongly disagreed with Ken's choice of quarry and would leave his friend to go it alone after "those common dames". No potential Mae Wests for him. Sadly, no birds of any kind had been snared by the end of term.

'Breaking-up' time triggered boisterous behaviour at HGS, including the showering of "confetti all over masters' cars", tying a tin can to the Art master's car, hoisting a "prefect's gown on to flagpole", and similar japes and larks in the best, good-natured rowdyism tradition.

*

After another fruitless foray in Perry Park;

"Let's give the girls a miss for a bit" – and this from Ken!

"Suits me fine – but sure you won't miss the girls a lot?"

"Oh, shut up!"

After this radical change of plan to a 'boys should be boys' regime, liberated from the thraldom of feminine allure – the two friends adjourned to Ken's back garden.

"I'll make the track," said Jim, "while you catch the runners."

"OK"

Jimmy set about building a running track from a heap of damp sand (or rather two adjoining tracks, grooves with sharply banked sides) with first a bend to the left – and then one to the right.

Ken soon returned from a distant part of the garden carrying an old jam jar, its open top covered by one hand.

"Here you are, which one do you want?"

"That one." Jim pointed.

"Right."

At the entrance to each groove was placed, with great care – a black beetle. But the 'bolshie little black beggars' would persist in trying to run upwards instead of along and had to be carefully nudged, stopped, and re-started with subtle, gentle movements from a twig of privet, golden privet. (The garden like the house, was a bit superior.)

"Mine's the winner, by a clear eight lengths. Hoo bloomin' ray."

"Another race?"

"No," Ken was already bored, "tell you what..."

"Isaac or James?"

"Oh, you and your bloomin' puns."

"Pun my soul, it's just a harmless family affliction."

"Let's go fishing."

"Where?"

"Oh, just off Wood Lane where that pond is, you know, by the derelict, old farmhouse."

"OK"

The beetles were carefully released into the 'wild' and the boys set off.

After half an hour, not a single stickleback had been caught. Frustration and pent up energy found release by knocking down slates from the farmhouse roof – Jim (scores approximate) seven, Ken nineteen (he was a fine fast medium bowler).

"What say we go to Kingstanding Baths tomorrow?"

"Suits me."

Came the morrow. With the bus trip to Kingstanding Circle behind them, the friends swam with exhilaration and delight in the spanking new, highly impressive baths. Even so, Jim didn't rate his chances any higher than previously, at swimming the English Channel.

More energy release followed in the evening with games of tipcat in the quieter roads around Ken's home. But as fatigue increased, so did mis-hits and the wooden 'cat', a bit like a crude cricket bail, but with tapered ends – hurtled perilously close to well-cleaned windows. The boys called 'close of play' moments before they expected the first angry householder to appear on his doorstep.

But all this self-imposed shunning of 'damsel delight' company couldn't possibly last much longer.

After the Sunday rest day, Ken made a suggestion;

"Let's take another dekko at Cherry Orchard shall we?" He knew well enough what he was up to – but didn't disclose his true plans, at that stage, to his still rather gullible friend.

"OK"

Jim was aware that, so far, they had only partly explored the Cherry Orchard area where a new owner/occupier housing development was steadily expanding – full of bathrooms and indoor lavs, Jim enviously supposed. But there still remained plenty of trees to climb, shrubbery and long grass to stalk around in.

Gradually Ken 'steered' his friend towards one particular tree – a leafy sycamore, trying to mask his rising excitement as he did so. Both boys began climbing steadily, from branch to sturdy branch.

"Can't you make less racket?" hissed Ken to his friend.

"Why? What's the matter? I haven't disturbed any birds."

"Perhaps not, but you will in a minute, if you keep up that bloomin' din. Well at least one, any way. Look over there and *don't* shake the boughs so much."

"I can't see anything special. I don't know what you're getting so het up about."

"Not there you twerp! Over there. Yes, I thought as much – there they are canoodling away. He's a lucky young so and so. I seem to recognise the girl but I've not seen her from this angle before."

Ken chuckled and Jim craned his neck to get a clearer look.

What Jim hadn't twigged was that August Bank Holiday Monday was probably the best, the brightest and busiest day of the year for courting couples. But he didn't fancy being a Peeping Tom – well, not from a tree anyway.

"I'm getting down."

"OK – let's stalk them then through the long grass."

Jim agreed to that for from a prone position and a sauve qui peut situation, he could be quickly on his feet and away, before the hapless suitor could set off in dishevelled pursuit of the caddish schoolboy spies.

Yet, the espionage turned out to be a bit of a frost really. Nothing dramatically exciting or enlightening occurred. Still it was rather useful to receive visible confirmation that cuddling could be cosily carried out in the languorously sprawling as well as the sitting and standing positions. Hm, might be worth remembering.

Holiday time, again. Ken left to stay with relatives in the northern territory of Derbyshire. Jim played a few desultory games of cricket with Doug and Terry Baker – boys who, like himself, had once lived in Crompton Road. But now, unlike himself, they lived in that brand new (owner/occupier) semi in Great Barr – and would soon be at the seaside once more.

All in all, Jim was relieved, glad and grateful to be invited to spend a few days away from No. 37, at his Aunt Millie's home near Dudley. There would surely be a chance to visit 'Bungies' again, in the company of lively cousins.

Recalling Bungies and the affection in which it was held, Jim thought it would be as well if he brushed up his knowledge of Black Country dialect. How had the *Dudley Herald* put things?

"'Er sed 'er wud an' 'er cud an' 'er shud, but 'er doe.

I wud ef I cud, but ef I cor 'ow con I?

'Ow many am there on we?"

Well, Aunt Millie had three, Uncle Enoch four and Auntie Mabel nine; but Jim didn't expect to see all sixteen Black Country cousins during this short stay. No, he'd be content to meet one or two of the younger ones at Windmill End, and he had always enjoyed the company of Aunt Millie's daughters, Liz – much his own age – and the younger Pam.

But now, he held some niggling doubts about Liz. Was she still the tomboy wench of years ago – that close companion of childish escapades? Like seeing who could trap the most wasps inside an empty jam jar – and who could zoom higher on the park swings. Did the old values still hold? Or had Liz stepped over that mysterious threshold into the 'Amami night' world of young ladies? Jim decided that there was nothing for it but to apply a test.

From the tiny back garden of the small council house, Jim picked up an old, grey tennis ball and went to look for Liz. He found her in the bijou kitchen/diner busy helping her mom with a rock cake mixture.

"When you've finished Liz, fancy a game of five stones?" He held out the tennis ball.

Liz wrinkled her nose with disdain.

"No thanks. That's kid stuff. I expect young Pam will be happy to give you a game."

'Young Pam' gave a shy smile and nodded agreement.

"But I'll come with you to Bungies later on if you like," said Liz.

"Fine."

Although she giggled a fair bit, especially at her own missed catches, Pam was no match for a seasoned Jimmy, experienced in the madcap ways of a bouncing ball, as it sharply struck one pebble after another from the chalked square on the paving slab set against the outside wall.

Soon it was time for picture going.

"Not quite like old times."

"No, not quite; nowadays we can sit together. But just mind what you do when you peel that orange."

The cousins giggled.

Dear old Bungies: that affectionate nickname had been given to the local picture house which in years past had witnessed as much action off the screen as on. At children's matinees, boys and wenches had been strictly segregated and periodically the air between them would be thick with flying apple cores and orange peel. Clearly Odeon or Regal, wouldn't suit but Bungies was just fine.

Strolling, on his own, from Aunt Millie's to Aunt Mabel's one morning, parallel with a typical Black Country cut, (canal to lesser breeds) Jim was reminded of vivid images from years past – images of fire, flame, acrid smoke, dancing shadows and sweating grim faced women – the nailers. In poky, open-doored 'brew houses', at the back of their terraced brick built cottages, these exploited women had laboriously hammered away, forging nails, by hand.

The holidays wore on – Len Hutton scored a record 364 in the test match against the Australians at the Oval. England declared at 903 for 7. Gorblimey O'Reilly managed to take 3 wickets – for 178! And England won the match by an innings and 579 runs. What a pasting!

The day of Hutton's record score was further brightened for Jim by a letter from Dave, on holiday with relatives in Stockport. Guffawing Dave – an old pal from primary school days who had suddenly disappeared to Wales for a few years and just as suddenly reappeared. He had become one of the group of six assorted heretics who unfailingly and sorely tested Mr Harry Martin's Christian forbearance every Sunday afternoon. Coming from a Welsh family, David was never entirely free of chapel influence, look you, but this in no way hampered his HGS schoolboy facetiousness;

"Dear Bean,

The weather has made a mistake and kept fine. I have not taken any Cascara Saglada tablets yet, as there is a sanitary inspector living next door. Je n'ai pas eu des affaires du coeur, which means I haven't had any heart-throbs yet, but I have hopes. But I think that even Romeo's style would be cramped here with my auntie, who is assiduously keeping me to the straight and narrow path. She caught me playing Monopoly with a couple of friends after chapel on Sunday evening, but after tactful handling, she 'coddled up' (patents pending), and so I was forgiven ... PS Seen the angel again?"

Jim wasn't sure. Which particular angel? Dave adored quite a few from afar. Maybe that's why they stayed angelic.

Around this time Jim made an important entry in his diary. "I got my 'Matric' today. Cheers!" A self-conscious demonstration of British phlegm? No fear, just a genuine straightforward reaction.

Cheery news too about his financial situation. While Jim didn't learn the details until later, he did know that his Maintenance Allowance from the Education Committee would be paid for another year. Eventually he found out that this allowance had been increased from £15 to £20 per annum – with full exemption from school fees. All conditional, of course, on his "satisfactory attendance, progress and conduct" and subject to review from time to time.

Well, there would be absolutely no problem with attendance. Progress would depend very much on the subjects studied and the quality of the teaching. Conduct might be a little more tricky. This could be influenced by distractions he encountered and the outlets chosen for his burgeoning energy. He was fast becoming sturdier and stronger – more ready and more able than in the past, for example, to clean out and re-organise the coalhouse to his dad's satisfaction.

And not only that, but to clean the upstairs windows back and front, for his mom. Dear old (all of forty-five) Mom who, as he well understood, no longer wished, with the lower half of the sash windows raised, to sit on the window sills of the bedrooms with her broadening beam to the street and passers-by – or to the coalmen and the dustmen who came up the entry into the yard. Besides, she was not well, and in mid-August had travelled to Exmouth to stay in a convalescent home. Next day.

"Got my own breakfast. Did housework. Seems strange without Mom."

A fortnight later, sanity, stability and civilisation were restored to the Norton household.

"Glad to see her. She has had a great time. Looks fit and well. Villa won."

So all was completely right with the world again – well, with the tiny part in which young Jim spun around. Good things were happening elsewhere too. The *Queen Mary* had set a new record for the Atlantic crossing east to west, and Jim's hero, Sidney Wooderson set a new world record for the half-mile at 1 minute 49.2 seconds.

Quite astonishing news broke from the football world. Bryn Jones was transferred from Wolves to Arsenal for a staggering record £13,000. Jim, fingering a 3d bit and a halfpenny in his pocket, tried to make sense of this staggering sum. Measured sensibly, 13,000 pounds equalled 3,120,000 pennies. Say he took a girl to the pictures one day – sat in good seats at a tanner a head – bought ice cream and chocolate – in all, lashed out a couple of bob perhaps. That transfer fee would finance 130,000 such plush cinema visits. Wow!

Put another way, 3,120,000 pennies represented 520,000 packets of 10 for 6d fags, of many brands. A nice lot of fag cards there and plenty of swaps into the bargain! Crikey!

But greater surprises were in store.

Early in September, with the start of a new school year looming, Jimmy began to 'knock about' not only with Ken, but Doug and Dave for stalking ventures through the well-trodden hunting grounds of the parks.

On Monday 12th September, three of the four – Ken, Jim and Dave "got to know" a twosome of wenches or, as recorded, "two very nice girls" in Perry Park. "Very nice girls" – the first time such praise had been entered into the diary! Things were indeed looking up!

Chapter Five

"Great Life in VI!"

"Well then, I'll go out with Irene and..."

"Oh no you won't. You've got the names wrong anyway, and I'm going with Mary."

"Is the dark-haired one Irene then?"

"Yes."

"Well she seems OK but I still want to go with Mary."

"Well, I've just told you – you're not going to – I am."

Ken flushed. Never before had his unspoken right to first choice been challenged. He sensed the strong emotion behind his friend's firm declaration and was well aware that Jim could be a 'stubborn little bugger' at times. So, with assumed indifference, Ken assented, temporarily, to the new order. As a committed philanderer, he would bide his time, while naturally keeping other options open.

Dave's name never featured in this heated discussion about probable runners in the possible Romance Stakes, a discussion which had taken place after the two friends had escorted Irene and Mary home that evening after a Guides meeting. While admiring the well turned out appearance of both girls, Jim thought that Mary looked 'a real snip' in her smart Guides uniform.

Of course, the day of Jim's rebellion would be of no consequence, tossed into the dustbin of historical irrelevance, if the girls failed to turn up for the following day's date. But turn up they did, and on a serenely sunny afternoon, the five youngsters (Dave doggedly tagged along) strolled up and down the towpaths of the Hamstead canal, chatting awkwardly of this and that.

"This" might concern school and some of the problems teachers and parents, caused for the taught. "That" could range widely over films and film stars; the Villa, (without stars, except perhaps Frankie Broome and Eric Houghton); over "my mother says..." and "my dad says ..." and "do you think there'll be a war?" That possibility seemed nonsensical, grotesque even, on such a peaceful, brightly sunny afternoon – with just the occasional canal barge sliding slowly and sedately through the water, gold ripples spangled at bow and stern.

Something was bothering Ken however. There was a certain viciousness about the way in which he kicked stones into the canal, thwacked the towpath hedge with a piece of jagged tree branch, scuffed up little clouds of ash with irritable movements of his feet. No, this wasn't part of his normal showing off routine when in the presence of – Margery, Elsie, Sue, Joan – or girls generally to whom he took a fancy.

Later that day, Ken made another stab, eloquent and passionate, at recapturing his bird allocation command – but Jim remained 'a stubborn little bugger' – and his diary entry was succinct. Ken "says he's crazy" (about her) "big sissy."

Such emotional turmoil in just a few days! Doubtless aware of, possibly flattered and certainly amused by the manoeuvres and posturings adopted by boys to impress girls, Mary had not yet given any clear signals as to her own preferences, if any.

Mary was just fourteen and her pal just fifteen. Both girls attended Rose Hill Road School, the 'Handsworth Grammar' for girls, part of the prestigious King Edward VI's foundation group of schools.

Like most girls in such age groups, with springtime charm, freshness and vitality all about them, Irene and Mary appeared 'very easy on the eye' – most decidedly so, Jim decided. Raven-haired Irene ("she walks in beauty, like the night..."- no, that's enough of that he thought) stood about the same height as Jim – and wavy brown-haired Mary, a little shorter. So, being fanciful (and he often was) if the girls ever wore high heels, a heady thought in itself, Jim believed he would feel far more comfortable with Mary and that Irene would be a better match for Ken.

Dreams of waltzes on the dance floor apart, it was not her height or her looks but Mary's personality that made Jim keen to seek and share her company. Naturally, he was not indifferent to her physical charms, no siree – or unobservant. At Grove Lane public baths on a Sunday morning, he noticed that she "looks a treat in a bathing costume. Oh Boy!"

"Oh Boy!" A "great life" in the sixth form seemed to await him as well. Jim felt he had been reborn into a new, exciting, stimulating school environment – one where he was allowed eighteen, he counted them again – yes, eighteen free periods a week for private study! Now he could concentrate on a subject he liked – English; a subject he partly liked – History; and two he could put up with and work reasonably diligently at – French and German.

Then there was "Oh Boy!" style football. After trial games, he was selected to be "2nd XI Footer captain." Yippee! Not only that, his friendship with Mary was now more than a week old, a length of attachment which was "a record for this year"! Gee whiz! A great life indeed.

But once again the fates frowned on zestful, adolescent joy.

"Looks like war. Hurt my ankle…at football."

Not one, but two impending calamities – probable hostilities on European battlefields – and a cessation of sliding tackles, preferably in the mud, on the football pitch. But, after bathing his ankle, the swelling went down and Jim heard, with great relief, that the leaders of the four great powers – Hitler and Musso for the nasties, Daladier and Chamberlain for the goodies – had agreed to confer in Munich.

Next day, (be prepared, whatever came out of Munich) Jim, with five fellow sixth formers, busied himself in distributing nearly 4,000 gas masks to local schools. He recalled that two of his uncles had been gassed in the 'last lot'. As a result, frail Uncle Frank, invalided out of the army, had died prematurely, and robust Uncle Sam still laboured, successfully, with only one sound lung, to keep his allotment highly fruitful and in tip-top condition.

Jim knew that the use of poison gas in World War I and Mussolini's gas attacks on Abyssinian tribesmen in 1936 had engendered a very real and widespread fear that mustard gas, and similar horrific substances, would be used if and when the balloon went up again. Jim filed away in his diary a macabre poem; a world away from Byron's work, he thought cynically.

"If you get a choking feeling
And a smell of musty hay,
You can bet your bottom dollar
That there's PHOSGENE on the way.

Peaceful geraniums may
Look pleasant in a bed.
Dodge their scent in wartime;
It's LEWISITE! you're dead!"

With gas masks distributed, the ankle tested by fearsome PT and found to be "OK", the "peace for our time" Munich Agreement signed, life perked up again. The Second XI won its first match, against Oldbury, 6-2. "Yippee!" once more.

Paradoxically, with a breathing space achieved, at some cost to the Czech nation, Jim became one of four volunteer members of a "suicide squad" for gym activities. On the very next day after enlistment, he narrowly escaped self-destruction. As he sprinted for the buck, Jim had no thoughts of a death or glory leap. It was simply that his plimsolls, as per usual, were not up to snuff, plain 'dodgy' in fact. A curled loose edge of sole caught the top of the buck and sent him sprawling. Yes, the same old trouble – worn out sports clobber.

Good old Ma moved into decisive action – "a good pair of Dunlop pumps 5/11" after an evening's shopping expedition with Mom – and a "nice raincoat and two shirts" into the bargain. A little hum for Mum seemed in order;

""Get your coat and get your hat,
Leave your worries on the doorstep,
Life can be so sweet
On the sunny side of the street..." "

'Trouble was,' mused Jim, 'was the well scrubbed doorstep at 37 big enough for all his Mom's worries?'

*

What with football, gymnastics, picture going, Guild activities, swimming, card playing – and the girlfriend – actual school lessons became something of a distraction from what really mattered in life. Still, private study periods provided a bonus in all sorts of ways. The more time that could be spent attempting to translate stilted literary English into fractured French in the form room, instead of back at the dump, the better. Wrestling with the wiles of Metternich and Talleyrand in the living room, could so easily be interrupted with the bugle call to 'put the kettle on son'. Then again, PS periods allowed some scope for a little relaxation.

The Head "caught 'Dandy' and I playing ping-pong. Gave us a talk on responsibility. Shall have to go easy during Private Study now."

That was simply an artful reminder not to be caught out so easily next time. Dandy and he would put their guileful sixth form heads, one ginger, one brown – together.

Despite some hiccoughs, Jim thoroughly enjoyed his first term as a sixth former. He greatly valued being treated as a young adult instead of a regimented boy. Now he could ask questions; just why did the Weimar Republic in Germany collapse? – instead of mechanically chanting German case endings:

der gute Mann   (Nominative)
den guten Mann   (Accusative)
des guten Mannes   (Genitive)
und so weiter,

as had been required by that likeable, but hopeless disciplinarian 'Gaydog', a prominent eccentric among the odder of the oddball teachers.

Jim, or better perhaps James, in this august context, was also quite bucked at having been made a prefect. Naturally enough, his pride didn't bear a candle to that experienced by his mom, who somehow produced a surfeit of clean handkerchiefs. He wasn't too bothered about the trappings of great office – a short black gown and a specially designed cap – all black, circled by two thin rings of gold stitching, and the school badge, also in old gold, set above the peak. And, as for having been appointed to late duties, along with 'Syd' Whitley, this responsibility was, on the whole, a blessing.

Jimmy luxuriated in being able to miss boring morning assembly. Yippee – and then some. 'Bridgebuilders' sounded far more tuneful through brickwalls, and, truth to tell, the Head's sermons, now muffled, far less boring. Late prefects stood at the school entrance to record the names of the unpunctual unwashed. Late prefects had, of course, to turn up early. No problem for Jim but a little more difficult for Syd who lived virtually on the doorstep.

Latecomers were allowed to offer excuses. Varied and ingenious did such excuses and 'excuses' prove to be. Sometimes, the scale on which chains came off bicycles reached epidemic proportions. Some parents wrote notes of apology for their offspring, sometimes in remarkably un-adult handwriting. It was difficult to sort out the genuine from the bogus. Syd and Jim tended towards a tender hearted approach to the problem, a problem often compounded by the weather.

Fogs were all too chokingly common during Birmingham winters. One sulphurous morning, the fog hung about in particularly dense and evil fashion – a bit like a highly recalcitrant fag, Jim thought. Why couldn't this vile concoction be bottled and exported to Adolf and Benito, Jim wondered. Before long, more boys were lolling, lounging and coughing in the corridors than had assembled in the hall. Finally, – "on sure foundations..." was totally submerged by the din kicked up by the multitude of latecomers.

Syd and Jim, anxious, flustered, paced rapidly up and down the corridors seeking to regain control – by persuasion, entreaty, cajolery, threats, 'bookings' to stand outside the Head's study – all to no avail. Din undiminished continued. A senior master – Baggy Brandon (he of the shapeless trousers) emerged from the hall to quell the racket. He too had scant success – fog and the mob triumphed – temporarily.

It was still chokingly foggy when Jim reached home late that afternoon. As he paused to unlatch the garden gate, he hoped his mom wouldn't hear him coughing as he sought to clear the sooty filth from his lungs. His mom could be such a worry pot.

No, all was well; Sal said simply:

"Fancy a cup of tea son? I expect you'll be glad to wet your whistle after being out in that muck. Just put the kettle on will you. I'll see to it in a minute. I just want to finish reading this bit about the Duchess of Windsor." Wilf snorted with disgust and winked at his son.

"Bloomin' parasites the pair of them."

"But she wears such lovely jewels! Just listen to this Wilf: "The Duchess wore a gown of very pale Wallis blue with a dazzling necklace of rubies and an enormous diamond and ruby clip...""

"Like I said – parasites, the pair of 'em!"

Sal sniffed and disappeared into the kitchen, doubtless dreaming of jewels that could never be hers.

Jim glanced casually at the magazine his mom had been reading.

"Uncle Sam been here and left this?"

"Yes – and one or two other copies over there." Jim looked at the sepia photos of the idle rich gorging themselves at a banquet in Cannes. At one table sat Marlene Dietrich wearing, "a white gown over which she had thrown a cape of swan's down." Opposite her sat Grace Moore.

Jim knew that his Dad had taken a fancy to operatic Grace – she did have such a glorious voice. He began singing very softly:

""One night of love,
When two hearts are one,""
"Di da di da di da..."
"Can you remember the rest of it, Dad?"
"Never you mind."
"Who's Erich Remarque?"
"Why do you ask?"
"Well, he's sitting at the same table as Grace and Marlene – oh yes, it says he's the German author of *All Quiet on the Western Front*."

"That's him. A film was made of the book, about seven or eight years ago. I think a chap called Lew Ayres played the hero. It's an anti-war film, like the book. I don't suppose it'll be shown now we have the Munich agreement, but that sell-out won't last."

Jim turned the pages of *Weekly Illustrated*.

There did seem to be quite a bit about war and war preparations in its forty lavishly illustrated pages – bomb damage to Hankow caused by Japanese air raids: crippled old soldiers, no more than 40 years of age perhaps, attending a party of the "Not Forgotten" Association at Buckingham Palace: the present army learning to camouflage tanks and guns down near the woods 'somewhere'. Two pages of photos of Britain's Air Minister – Sir Kingsley Wood: two centre pages for striking photographs of the Home Fleet on autumn manoeuvres: air raid precautions in a Kent village.

"Do you think there'll be a war Dad?"

"Yes, sooner or later the balloon's bound to go up again. Probably sooner."

His voice sounded grim and bitter.

Jim turned to cheerier pages depicting slim, long legged American girls – some British as well. ""Jitterbugs" go places." His interest was caught not just by the legs and happy faces, but by the new lingo: "Jam session", "jive", "whackey", "killer diller", "cutting rugs".

He'd hold a few of these expressions in reserve, in case Dave, always the one for being 'up' with fashion, tried to impress him.

"There's no need for you to keep gawping at those shameless hussies showing too much of what they shouldn't show. In my day, a pretty ankle was enough to turn a man's head."

Sal, who had just brought in the cups of 'steaming golden brown' looked archly at her husband who kept his features as still as Buster Keaton's.

Jim sought safer ground.

"How about this Persil advert then." He read out, ""Mrs Toole, of Norbury, says: Twenty-one years ago I was given this tea-cloth as a wedding present...naturally I've always washed it with Persil, and today it looks as good as new.""

"Well, tea-cloths are one thing, your bloomin' football shorts are quite another. I don't know how you get them so muddy, I really don't. Whatever Persil does, I still have to use a lot of good old-fashioned elbow grease to get your shorts anywhere near presentable."

On those wonderfully muddy football fields, Jim was experiencing mixed fortunes, the 2nd XI's form being very in and out. After the initial victory, a right thrashing, a defeat at home 0 - 6. A measured analysis of the game followed: "they", (Holly Lodge) "were much the better and bigger side." The following Wednesday, (Wednesday afternoon for sports, Saturday morning attendance at school for classes) "lost to Dudley 0 - 8"; the game being summed up by the HGS left back and captain as, "the defence is all right but forwards are awful." A biased appraisal surely? Not altogether: "2 XI want me on committee so we can pick a decent team."

After that a few more games were won and rather more lost. But never was there a goal famine. Some games were rained off (usually because of waterlogged pitches) but in the dozen games actually played, HGS scored 30 to the oppositions' 57. 7 plus goals a game - good value for the handful or so of spectators. Such statistics concealed some trouncing defeats - but Jim was not present for all of them. Occasionally he was picked, sometimes at embarrassingly short notice, to play for the first eleven - again with high scoring results - a home defeat against Dudley 2 - 5 and a superb win 10 - 2 against West Bromwich.

His diary best explained the 'embarrassment' of - 'short notice'.

"Curse! I have got to play on Firsts on Saturday. So I can't go to fair. Very disappointed. Contemplated getting injured at gym etc. Still I can't let school down. Wrote letter to M explaining everything. Suggested alternatives. Went to Guild. Mr Butler 4th Dimension. Good. I was a bit preoccupied."

Crikey, who wouldn't be? The 4th dimension has been a taxing concept at any time, but when one has a troubled mind, and an even more troubled heart – phew!

So there it was – yet one more example (at age fifteen) in mankind's long history of the oftimes desperate struggle between love and duty. Not quite in the same heroic mould perhaps as Mark Antony's dilemma – stay to lead the Egyptian fleet or hurry to the side of the languishing, heaving-bosomed Cleopatra? (But troublesome enough at 15.)

Besotted Antony lost both the battle of Actium and the ravishing beauty of the Nile. Jim not only did his duty, in a 2 all draw against an Old Boys' XI   "1st pt firsts have got!" – but won a fabulous bonus into the bargain.

But what kind of 'contemplated injury' might Jim have suffered to keep his afternoon date with Mary? A twisted ankle perhaps – there did seem to be a weakness in one – remember Munich? But the outcome of 'accidents' cannot be finely judged. What if it turned out that he couldn't even hobble to meet Mary?

And then again he wondered, what had his moral, love v duty dilemma signified? Was it love of Mary's company that spurred him on – or love for the girl herself? No, that latter idea was still a bit too scary to consider, with Mary only fourteen years and two months of age.

All idle speculation again, for practical Mary had sorted out the dating difficulty. Being the personable girl she was (the firm chin and well defined lips offered significant clues) it turned out that Mary had been able to persuade her parents to let her go to the famed Onion Fair in the evening.

And so, on the gritty, ash-covered Serpentine Ground, near hallowed Villa Park, a quite magical time was shared by Mary and Jim.

Fairgrounds seemed so much more exciting at night, when the myriad constellations of varied coloured lights, many twinkling, came into their own against the pitch black sky. The youngsters strolled, sometimes hand in hand, from one centre of gaudy light and blaring noises, to another, each set in mysterious pools of shifting, shadowy darkness.

Together they experienced the giddy motions of the waltzer, the dodgems, the big wheel, the roundabouts – the even giddier emotional thrills of the boxing booth, Wall of Death, the ghost train – and, best of all, holding hands "a lot of times".

Jim took Mary home. Her parents were out. She invited him in. Shuffling his feet, he blushingly, apologetically declined. One of his Dad's music-hall songs came unsummoned into his head: "I'm shy Mary Ellen, I'm shy..." But shyness wasn't the real reason for the refusal. Oh dear no. The plain fact was: "it was 10 o'clock."

On his way home, half-walking, half-running, he thought to himself, 'what a mutt,' to pass up such a chance – for maybe the first kiss, and real cuddle. He vowed to cultivate cunning defiance of maternal 'tyranny' – to try and kick into touch the feelings of guilt that arose if he knew he would be displeasing his mom by being late.

*

By the time Christmas was being seriously saved for, Mary and Jim had established a pattern of regular meetings, almost like an established courting couple. They met on Monday evenings after Guides, Saturday evenings at the Villa Cross picture house, Sunday mornings at the public baths, Sunday evenings after church, at Mary's church.

Scooting from his own church to St Marys C of E, Hamstead Road by the park, Jim wondered, self mockingly, whether he might have imperilled his soul. In order to be on time for his date, he sometimes left the Congregational church before the sermon had droned to a finish and before the blessing had been given. Without misgiving, he accepted the risk and sped on, stopping briefly at the corner confectioners in Putney Road, to buy, for his special girl, the special weekly treat of – Smarties.

This regular pattern of planned meetings was supplemented whenever possible. Mary came to the HGS Speech Day, school plays, and eventually to the Guild. Sometimes the youngsters met, as if by chance, on the way home from school. Then they would walk part of the way together before Mary headed for a new owner occupier house in Cherry Orchard – lucky thing. There was sure to be a bathroom there and that 3d tablet of soap for schoolgirl complexion – all over. Whew!

For such frequent meetings and inevitable last minute changes to some plans, an effective communications system was essential. This emerged in the form of a small boy, a fag at HGS, Mary's younger brother Dickie.

Dickie, a typical 'cheeky young devil' embarked on a part-time career as confidential courier, for it was he who passed, forth and back, the scribbled notes between his sister and her boyfriend. Sometimes young Dick would trail after Mary and Jim on some of their many walks, in the way younger brothers did in the 1930s when older sisters had, for reasons best known to themselves, begun to take an interest in older boys.

How to deal with him? Jim could not threaten (though he "felt like murdering him") let alone inflict physical retribution. Dickie was in too powerful a position in the communications network. Nor did Jim have the means to buy him off in the time honoured tradition of – 'here's a tanner, take yourself to the pictures, pronto.'

Sometimes the dogged shamus could be shaken off in a dense, coal burning induced fog. Usually though, the solution lay in Mary giving Dickie a good talking to, at a discreet distance from Jim, emphasising the points she was making with energetic gestures – one or two of which may well have smartly clipped Dickie's ear. All in all though, Dickie did sterling service as a messenger.

Throughout this period of budding romance, Ken and Dave bobbed erratically on and off the stage of the dating game. Sometimes both would turn up, with Jim, to meet the girls after Guides – sometimes one, sometimes neither. The same with picture going. Mary and Jim didn't much care – content, as they were, in each other's company. But it was a bit rough on Irene, a sensitive girl, whose full lower lip quivered whenever her feelings were hurt.

Perhaps it was an accident; perhaps it was deliberate; but ardent, volatile Celt that he was, Dave (fed up with Ken's rivalry) chose 7th November to deliver the blow that 'he was finishing with Irene' – yes, 7th November – a night of highest delight for astronomers! The moon's total eclipse! And for Irene, who knew what hopes were blotted out? She was certainly "very upset".

8th November: "I can see Dave regrets his decision already. Silly dope!"

But the moon reappeared. So did Dave, so did Irene. Ken too – Jim's rebellion had not been forgotten or forgiven.

Chapter Six
Roll On Christmas

""When father papered the parlour
You couldn't see Pa for paste,
Dabbing it here, dabbing it there,
Dabbing it every, everywhere.
Ma got stuck to the ceiling,
Kids got stuck to the floor,
I've never seen a family *so stuck up* before.""

Jim grinned as he listened to the old music hall ditty. For him, the cream of the joke lay in its ironic quality. Quite unlike 'Pa', his own dad took good care to keep well out of the way whenever paper hanging, painting, interior decorating of any kind, was being undertaken. He hated any 'upset' of that sort and made no bones about it. He, Wilf, would never be stuck up either with paste – or social pretension.

Whether his dad had got the words of the song quite right, Jim couldn't be sure. But 'sans fairy Ann' as the Tommies used to say in the trenches, 'melody' in the home meant that his singing sire was, most definitely, in a good mood. Presumably Wilf's gammy leg was not playing him up. And he must surely have enough coppers in his pocket to send Jim to the outdoor across the road, later in the evening for a jug of ale. Jim waited. Yes, here it came, an unrequested encore:

""I'm getting ready for me mother-in-law,
I'm getting ready for the fray...
There's a little old room
On the third back floor,
Where the beetles up the wall they climb,
Oh mother, mother, mother, mother,

You'll have a lively time!" "

"You should be ashamed of yourself, you old donkey."
Sal pursed her lips.
"My mother was a gem – and you know it."
"So she was. I don't deny it. But I wasn't having a dig at her or your precious family. Here son," he handed Jim a florin.
"Nip over the road and fetch your mother a milk stout – oh, and a packet of crisps for yourself. Your mom seems to be having a fit of the megrims again."

Jim himself had recently begun to wonder what was 'up' with his mom. She didn't seem her usual self, being 'touchy' about anything that concerned herself, however remotely. Take that incident of a few days ago.

With his parents seated in their respective, jointly creaking, easy chairs either side of the fireplace and Jim at the table (doing less scratching let it be said – but he was holding a newspaper) – a discussion had arisen about 'life' and its 'purpose'.

In his newly found 'intellectual' liberation as a sixth form scholar, Jim had begun to question the hitherto unquestionable.

"Well, no-one asks to be born and none of us choose our parents."

At this point, his mom had partly stifled a sob and looked reproachfully at her 'only chick'. Tears began to slide slowly around her chubby cheeks. She sobbed again, dabbed at her eyes with her pinny – but said nothing.

Jim knew that he would have to stop this 'line of enquiry' – but he made one last stab to combat emotion with reason.

"Mom, believe me, I'm not getting at you, it's nothing personal. You know that don't you Pop?"

"Yes son," Wilf nodded his agreement, "but do remember your Mom's thyroid trouble."

'How could he ever forget?' Jim wondered. He was reminded of that troublesome condition often enough, and had begun to doubt its validity as an explanation of much that puzzled him.

As he got to his feet, florin in hand, Jim wondered why it was that women, at least those of his acquaintance, seemed incapable of discussing in a sensible manner, the great abstractions of life? Whatever was discussed seemed always to return to their own personal position and emotions and to leave to one side their general role in the scheme of things. Sir Walter Scott had surely been right when he had written;

"O Woman! in our hours of ease,
Uncertain, coy, and hard to please
And variable as the shade
By the light quivering aspen made."

Jim conceded ('fair play's a...') that the next couplet was also probably accurate:

"When pain and anguish ring the brow,
A ministering angel thou!"

He'd probably find out some day he thought.

But believing also that too much reflection could addle the brain, and that action was often a good cure for pithering thinking, Jim went for the milk stout – and his packet of Smiths' crisps, with its twist of blue paper containing salt.

As he sauntered back from the off-licence, Jim none the less reflected that there was much more to music than his Dad's Victorian sentimental ballads and music hall songs. 'Joshua, Joshua' with his 'sweeter than lemon squash you are' – and 'Darling I am growing o-old, silver threads among the gold,' were well enough in their way but sadly dated.

Jim recognised that he had grown to like certain hymns, especially the rousing, 'tub thumping' ones like 'Onward Christian Soldiers' and 'Jerusalem'. Best of all though was the softer, gentler 'The day thou gavest Lord is ended' for this marked the end of what had usually been a tedious service, and often the start of that scampering 'Smarties run' to romance. But when, in April, *Elijah* had been presented by the HGS choir at the prestigious St. Martin's Church in Birmingham's Bull Ring, Jim's syntax had buckled under the strain of trying to express his appreciation of classical music.

"Singing OK But music rotten except for a few."

Still, even in that inelegant and jarring critique glimmered a ray of hope that he might yet turn out to be a low middle-brow – joining the ranks of the many who simply liked the 'best bits' – the 'eclectic approach' when you were swanking.

He had certainly enjoyed the best bits of the school's presentation of Gilbert and Sullivan's *Pirates of Penzance* where, as shown in a school photo, Dave had put on display a fine pair of piratical legs. *Pirates* was much more to Jim's taste than the previous production, *Iolanthe* with all those fairies prancing about. It was the catchy tunes in these operettas that he liked, not the rambling, part-talking, part-singing, largely unintelligible chunks in between.

But best of all, he liked many of the tunes played by the dance bands, Jack Hylton, Ray Noble, Henry Hall and the like – 'on the air' – or on 78s in friends' homes. Here was melody, simple phrases maybe, but they could be hummed, whistled, sung; played on the mouth-organ. Happy songs to lighten hard times, sad songs, sentimental songs, daft songs – 'When it's night time in Italy, it's Wednesday over here.' Songs of love, of romance – but rarely of marriage.

*

""A fine romance my friends this is,
A fine romance with no kisses...""
Jim whistled to himself as he knotted his school tie, and made ready for his date. For over two months now he had been going out with a girl of whom he had become very fond. 'Smitten with' – was perhaps nearer the mark.
""Gosh, I must be falling in love,
Can't sleep at night,
Got no appetite...""
No, quite decidedly no, that did not describe his condition. All twaddle really. He slept soundly and hadn't gone off his grub. Far from it. The weekly plate of bacon and egg in particular was devoured with the utmost relish, and all other meals with keen enjoyment. No, that other song in his head had perhaps been nearer the mark:
""I haven't got a chance,
This is a fine romance.""
Two months already and he still hadn't ventured to kiss Mary. As he slipped into his navy blue gabardine raincoat, and fastened the belt, he wondered what a real kiss would be like. Quite different, he imagined, from the affectionate pecks exchanged with girl cousins.

What he hoped for, some day, was the type of kiss his brother Ted had once described as a 'real plonker'. Perhaps he'd 'have a go' tonight.

"See you later. And before you ask – yes, I have got a clean hanky."

"Cheerio son, no hanky-panky mind."

"Like I said – yes, I have got a hanky and yes, it is clean. But what do you mean by 'panky' Mother dear? You've never really told me have you? A lad should know these things."

"Oh get along with you, you cheeky young so and so. You take after your Uncle Les you do."

His mother gave him an affectionate push towards the front door.

Had there been a twinkle in his mother's eye? She must have noticed that Fred Astaire tune he had been humming – "a fine romance with no kisses". No matter. Tomorrow perhaps he'd be whistling, ""The touch of your lips...such tenderness lies in their soft caress..."

It was not to be. As usual, when he thought the right moment had arrived, his courage failed him. He knew timing was important and that rebuffs could be wounding, especially if you were sensitive and lacking in the sorbo rubber qualities of debonair Ken. So he waited, yet again – until a week or so before Christmas.

Icy winds blasted in from polar regions. Oh bitter, bitter chill it was. So cold, so blood freezingly cold, that the Sunday evening walk after church was shortened to escorting Mary straight home. Jim made his clumsy move, made clumsier by the arctic conditions. He was duly rebuffed. What girl, even a hardy, sporty tomboy, in her right mind, would want to kiss a shivering red-nosed schoolboy in such shrivelling conditions.

"Had a good time son? You look perished. Come and sit by the fire. Just budge over a bit, you old donkey."

Thawing out, Jim wrote: "Made a fool of myself. Curse." Then, his thoughts moving forward to early January, his mood brightened. Irene and Mary planned a party – to be held at Mary's home on 4th January, 1939. Jim had been invited. He knew, mostly from hearsay rather than direct experience, that parties could mean 'high jinks' and, maybe, kissing games. Goody, goody!

He wasn't sure whether he really remembered, or only remembered what he had been told by grown-ups, about *that* rollicking, drum-busting family shindig, Dolly's wedding reception, legendary in its way, and still talked of with chortling delight by the survivors.

At the 'old home' around 1927, garlands of fashionable Chinese lanterns had been hung in the lilac trees. Indoors, a hired band played hot jazz, thumping hot jazz. Time and again sweating dancers flung themselves, with growing inebriated vigour, strings of beads (on the ladies) swirling violently, into the Charleston. Bertie, the best man, bashed his foot through the big drum, to universal laughter and applause – drummer excepted. Floor boards and their joists (above the cellar) sagged and swayed. (They still did when Jim was a Meccano model building boy, a light weight boy: to that Jim could readily testify.)

Came the head splitting dawn. Uncle Les, dressed as a Corner House 'Nippy' served trifle, cold custard and jelly to the still half-sozzled guests strewn all over the house – including that unknown half-clad chap, sprawling spark out in the bath. A working class Bacchanalia if ever there was one. Freedom for just a few short, fun packed hours, from poorly paid grinding work – or the grinding worries of the dole.

Jim didn't expect any such 'Roaring 20s', Jazz Age antics on 4th January. And before then, he had a problem to resolve, or rather two.

*

"I met Mary and Irene from Guides last night."

"So what?"

"So they have invited me to go to their party on January 4th. They would like you to go as well – and have asked me to ask you."

"Is Ken going?"

Jim fidgeted uneasily, but that truth telling training had been rigorous, and duly triumphed. His plans to follow the girls' devious scheme of 'don't let the other boy know', collapsed.

"Well, he's been invited. But I haven't seen him yet."

"Well, I shan't go if he goes. He's always mucking things up."

"Well, you can talk, you're the one who eclipsed Irene's hopes a few weeks ago. She was very upset at the time you know."

Dave scowled. And then a broad grin spread across what had been a sourly discontented face. He broke into a loud guffawing laugh as the penny dropped about the eclipse 'joke'.

"Your tongue's a bit too sharp sometimes Jim. One of these fine days you'll cut your own throat."

Jim made no reply – and then said, "So, what shall I tell them?"

Dave returned to glowering.

"Oh, buzz off and see what Ken says."

Jim did.

"I met Mary and Irene from Guides last night."

"What a surprise!"

Jim ignored the sarcasm. Such remarks were ten a penny in his own home – and in those of his brothers and sister. His mother, of gentler stock than the family she had married into, never tired of trotting out; 'you know, sarcasm is the lowest form of wit'.

"They'd like you to go to their party on January 4th."

"Is Dave going?"

"I don't know."

"Typical."

With a scornful toss of the blonde, curly head, Ken continued, "Tell them I'll consider it."

Oh crikey – anger from Dave, hauteur du seigneur from Ken to contend with. The girls didn't seem too fussed. Perhaps the uncertainty added spice to the projected party, even if it slightly complicated calculations about the quantities of sausage rolls, mince-pies and jellies needed. Jim could imagine that Mrs Leigh might well say to her daughter, 'oh, I shouldn't worry – probably all three will turn up, you'll see. Boys at that age are touchy you know.'

Jim continued, sporadically, to persuade his two friends to 'come to the aid of the party.'

*

Christmas neared and customary preparations were set in train to enjoy a rollicking good time. Both customary and unusual preparations really. The sweep came to clean the 'parlour' fireplace and chimney in readiness for their very first roasting since the dump had taken in its new tenants. Jim put up the home-made paper chains – and cut his finger on the holly. The weather stayed bitterly cold– a double shiver for Jim when he recalled that botched attempt at a first kiss. Snow fell, slides and snowball fights followed. All in all, it looked like being a Christmas worth remembering. Would it be the last one in peacetime for a while?

When you thought about it (mused Jim) things did look a bit grim. On the 1st December the Government had revealed its plans for a National Register. These set out what everyone was to do if peace turned to war.

Quakers and friends at the Guild all seemed to be opposed to the notion, which to them appeared to mean that direction of labour would be introduced – with the consequent loss of individual freedom. Resolutely, Mary and Jim, friends but not Friends, took a robustly differing view that there would be no freedom at all if we did not organise efficiently to defend the country.

Then later in the month, the Government had announced its spending plans for providing air raid shelters. "Peace for our time"? 'Maybe if you are already well into your nineties', thought a slightly cynical Jim. 'Still, let's get the Christmas shopping done and worry about the state of the world some other time.'

"Went to Co-op and bought my Christmas presents."

This wasn't the first or last time that the Birmingham Co-operative Society featured in Jim's diaries. His own family circle and many, many similar working class families, held fast to three bedrock practices for survival and self-respect:

Vote Labour
Shop at the Co-op
Support the Villa

Black Country relatives could be excused, (just), from supporting the Villa and allowed to shout themselves hoarse for the Baggies (West Bromwich Albion) or the Wolves (Wolverhampton Wanderers).

*

"Jim."

"Hm?"

"I hope you're not thinking of buying me a Christmas present?"

Actually, Jim had been thinking of a free gift; hopefully more than one, if he could scrounge a piece of mistletoe, find the right secluded spot, and judge the right moment for amorous action.

"Of course I am. In fact, I'm quite determined to."

"Well, I do hope you won't."

Inwardly Jim groaned. Here he was again, confronted with what he took to be a typical female ploy. Did Mary really mean what she said? Or the exact opposite? A little probing seemed called for.

"Why ever not?"

Mary, (unusually for her), looked uncomfortable and stayed silent for a moment or two.

"Well, I'd really rather you didn't."

"And what sort of answer is that?"

"Well," – and again Mary looked ill at ease – "it's just that my mother thinks it wouldn't really be right for you to buy me a present."

"Oh, why ever not?"

"Mom says we've only known each other a short while and..." her voice and head dropped.

"Well, I make it three months, ten days and..." Jim looked at his watch, "almost three hours. Quite long enough. Quite long enough, I would have thought."

Mary laughed and gave his arm an affectionate squeeze with her gloved hand.

"You can be a chump at times – but a nice chump."

"A sixth form chump anyway, who's determined, nay very determined to buy you a Christmas present."

*

And so, it was from the local Co-op that Jim bought his first real present for his first real girlfriend. (And "what a girl".) He had remained totally unpersuaded by the 'arguments' of mother and daughter Leigh. Maybe that had been their firm intention, or more likely their firm hope all along? Oh, the wiles of wimmen! He smiled inwardly, for not so long ago, as a juvenile dimwit, he had thought of girls as simply being, well, simperers. Some still were of course, but Mary, "what a girl", was so refreshingly different.

More and more Mary revealed the tomboy side of her nature, being prepared to walk miles, simply miles with Jim by her side, to explore caves by the River Tame and the flooded basement of an abandoned priory, to ferret around old houses and partly built new houses, to tackle the giddy challenges of the fairground, to wallop Jim at table tennis. Yes, a girl like that richly deserved a fine Christmas present.

A few days before Christmas, to Jim's immense delight, snow began to fall and settle – "deadening, muffling, stifling..." and all the rest of it. During the afternoon of the day before Christmas Eve, Jim accompanied Mary on a long, tiring but exhilarating tramp through snow covered fields near Hamstead. After losing their way, more than once, and with feet chilled and damp, they stumbled back to the outskirts of Cherry Orchard as the late afternoon dusk deepened.

"Just stop a mo' will you."

"No, come on, it's getting dark. Mom will be getting anxious and if Dad's got home he will be getting cross."

"Please! I won't take a minute."

"Hurry up then – but you can't be that puffed out – you're always telling me you want to be a cross country runner."

"No, it's not that. It's just that..."

Jim fished into the damp pocket of his bedraggled raincoat.

"Here's your Christmas present. Happy Christmas and many of them."

With an awkward flourish Jim handed over a "½lb box of Black Magic" chocolates.

Mary's cheeks already rosy from the cold air and exertion of struggling through snow, took on a rosier colour still.

"Thank you very much indeed, Jim. What a lovely surprise. It's very sweet of you."

"And now the sweets are with you."

"Chump!"

They both grinned.

"No, it really is very kind of you."

Mary smiled at him with obvious affection.

Dare he? No, better not. Although the weather was not as arctic as at the time of his first and dismal attempt at a kiss, even such a sporty girl as Mary, with doubtless chilled feet, and certainly pink nose, would be readier to be kissed when she was warm, dry – and in a cosy corner somewhere.

But on Christmas Eve, Jim felt it necessary to record wistful regrets.

"Wish I had used the mistletoe yesterday."

Even though the sprig had become a bit squashed in his other, non Black Magic raincoat pocket, it was still, even in fading light, recognisably mistletoe. Ah well, roll on 4th January, 1939.

*

Sunday – and Christmas Day, the first white Christmas for ten years – an excellent start. But for Jim it "seemed strange not to have a pillow case" filled with presents. He was reminded that 'he was getting too old for that sort of thing now'. Too old maybe, but not too young to enjoy the high spot of the day – the traditional card playing session at Uncle Sam's.

Uncle Sam, wife and daughter lived in one of a terrace of six poky, grime-stained, brick built cottages near Wood Lane. These Englishmen's castles were divided in the centre by a tunnel entry. Set at right angles from the back of each end cottage, ran a low line of wash-houses and the shared lavatory. A bit of a bugbear design that, entailing a lurching walk along the cracked, uneven, slimy brick path, to seek relief – especially hazardous on wild black nights of lashing rain and Siberian winds. And then to find some neighbour had pipped you to it! 'Shan't be a minute' – a minute that seemed a writhing eternity.

But on Christmas night 1938 all was conviviality and good cheer– hearty, respectable working class good cheer. No effin', no blindin'– sauciness yes, coarseness no.

Jim glanced with affection at the familiar, respected, loved and now glowing, reddening faces. In the tiniest of all the tiny working class 'parlours' he had known, sat eight people. A veritable furnace of a coal fire had set the chimney a roaring. The room seemed stiflingly hot and almost airless. Faces glistened in the light of the leaping flames. Jackets and cardigans had been shed, waistcoats, collars and ties well loosened.

Uncle Sam, quiet and undemonstrative, made a generous host. His wife – gentle, sickly Aunt Nell, smiled placidly – safe in the knowledge that her overflowing cupboard of patent medicines was handily placed, just in the next room. Their daughter, Eileen, round faced and ginger haired – a young lady now with 'a nice office job', but still the giggle of a school-girl, sat next to her 'Auntie Sal'. Harold was there, so was Les. Slightly to one side again, sat Grandad contentedly puffing away at his twist filled pipe.

A game of Newmarket; hitherto in full gallop, had come to a temporary halt. Les, naturally, was banker. He was an acknowledged and admired master at shuffling and dealing cards – dextrous, very quick – and fair. Just a touch impatient perhaps.

"Come on Sal, stop the cag-magging. Stop pulling the poor woman to pieces."

The ladies present had taken a brief pause to savour a juicy titbit of local gossip involving the milkman, maybe the bread roundsman, maybe even the coalman – and certainly some woman who somehow, 'was no better than she should be' and whose late husband had been pushing up the daisies for only a few weeks.

Sal put her tongue out at her youngest brother. Les had been used to that since early childhood and simply grinned.

"Oh, come on, do leave the poor woman alone. Anyhow, you can say what you like, it's only natural that she should want a bit of company. And, fair dos, it has to be admitted that she has a lovely pair of -"

"Ankles?"

"Ruby red lips?"

"Roguish brown eyes?"

"Before I was so rudely interrupted," Les affected mock gravity, "I was going to say," he paused, (but only slightly, as he caught his sister's warning glance), "a lovely pair – of china dogs – on the mantelpiece."

"First time I've heard 'em called that," murmured Eileen as she nudged her elbow into Aunt Sal's ribs.

"Oh, and how would you know?"

Les assumed a nonchalant air. "Oh, the butcher told me. Now for Pete's sake -"

"Oh, so that's what he's called!"

"...let's get on with the game. Who's got the ten of diamonds?"

"Sorry, I have."

"Jack?"

"Yes, me!"

With a squeal of delight, Sal swept off from the upturned 'runner', a small heap of coins including that "little bit of snow" – a "silver" 3d piece – a "little Joey".

Jim was delighted for his mom and wondered vaguely whether they'd all have such a jolly time next year – if by then Britain should be at war. His reflections became hazy and confused, for plied with a mixture of port and pop (another step towards approaching maturity) only the present seemed to matter.

At the end of 1938, Jim took stock, not of life, world events or his wardrobe – but of just a few of life's simpler aspects – for example, Christmas presents he had been given. These included not one but "two ties" – from Brenda of Babbacombe. He still scented possible danger. Nearly eighteen months had gone by since he had last seen that voluptuous siren. Was the widowed mother still urging her daughter to keep the friendship alive, with some view to ensnaring that big softy – Uncle Harold? Not one but "two ties". The stakes had obviously risen. As he had more than once reflected, and was to continue to reflect – really, you never did know with ladies, did you?

Back on surer ground, Jim the picture-goer recorded that during the year he had been to the pictures thirty-two times, nine times in the company of Mary.

No doubt at all about his top three films;

1   *Snow White and the Seven Dwarfs*
2   *The Drum*
3   *Oh Mr Porter* – a good laugh with Will Hay and his cronies.

Snow White – the film, not the slightly soppy character, had been enchanting when holding hands with his own charmer at the Villa Cross. Jim had revelled in the antics of the dwarfs and the jolly, jigging music at the party held for Snow White. Golly! Irene and Mary's party was very near now. Which dwarf did he, Jim, most resemble? he wondered. Certainly not Grumpy – dependent on his mood that might be Dave's part – partly Bashful, partly Doc – most decidedly Happy, if wishful thinking became reality.

Chapter Seven
Taking a Grip

Wednesday 4th January, 1939 began in bright and spritely fashion. "Cleared snow away and had a snow fight with some kids." A sure fire way of making the blood tingle. ('Hopefully,' Jim thought, 'there would be even tinglier tingling later that day, which would have nothing to do with snow.') Dave "rolled up" and another tussle ensued – this time with words flying like snowballs. After a sustained bombardment, Dave yielded, and agreed, grudgingly, to turn up for the Cherry Orchard fiesta.

Thanks, in no small measure, to Queen Victoria, the girls' party proved to be truly and wonderfully exciting – at least as far as Jim was concerned. Many debts are owed by their descendants, to the Victorians and not just for the legacies of worthy but sober– bridges, railways and public works – but immensely jolly parlour games such as 'Postman's Knock'. Phew, at last Mary and Jim had their opportunity in a socially approved kissing game. They joyfully seized it – and one another.

"Had Mary about seven times in Postman's Knock. We worked it great. Oh boy, what a thrill!"

Not quite the carefully turned elegance of an Elizabethan love sonnet, but then, Jim was not writing for a courtly audience, or anyone else for that matter. He continued, Mary looked "an absolute dream" in her new party frock, with its short sleeves and pretty pleats; a young, attractive girl, radiant with health, high spirits and happiness.

Of course, those kisses were clumsy, over eager and a little hurried – but sweet, oh so sweet – the first sweetheart kisses either had experienced.

To have lingered in order to learn and enjoy, would have been unsporting and almost certainly unwise. Nearby, in the room from which the 'Addressee' had been summoned by the romantic postman (or post girl), other laughing lads and lasses excitedly awaited their belated mail. Mary's watchful parents were never far away to ensure discreet observance of 'Marquess of Victoria' rules. It was perhaps a shrewd tactical move on Jim's part, that he kissed Mary's mother under the mistletoe.

Those first kissing exchanges between Mary and Jim, though sweetly thrilling, and for Jim 'streets ahead' of affectionate pecks, still fell short of Ted's description of 'real plonkers'. Jim didn't much care for that expression but warmly approved of its underlying sentiment, and so he added one more to his 1939 resolutions, to engineer, how best he might, some real, unhurried kissing with Mary, in conditions of privacy.

Dave had kept his word and come to the party. His Celtic moods accompanied him – elation one moment, dejection the next – predictably, Ken maintained his reputation for blithe flirtation and made "a date with a girl called Julie".

After the party – the hangover. But, truth to tell, not a severe one. School resumed. But for Jim, familiar and pleasing patterns fell back into place: 2nd XI football captain; Thursday evenings at the Guild. Motion: 'That the Englishman thinks too much of sport.' Ken and Jim agreed, without hesitation, to oppose such a self-evidently barmy motion. Dates with Mary, walks and talks, a visit to the panto; "Robinson Crusoe ... an excellent show. Four girl contortionists A.1." ('Well, no one who was C.3. could possibly have gone through those bizarre convolutions,' thought Jim.)

And then – top of the bill:

Sunday evening, "15th January. Started to rain when I left her. Kissed her goodnight. Great. Took some pluck. She returned it. Oh boy, oh boy, oh boy!"

Timing on this occasion ten out of ten; performance, still room for improvement, say seven out of ten. Jim looked forward eagerly to further practice.

"Such tenderness lies in their soft caress..."

That lyricist was spot on.

And boy, oh boy, just remember: "she returned it."

Though his heart was dancing with delight, "It's June in January because I'm in love...", some burdensome thoughts still came to trouble Jim's mind. First there was trouble with jittery Julie, and then the affair of the red hot poker.

Jim learned, (via Dickie), that Julie had experienced "a nervous breakdown." What had Ken said, or even worse, done? He certainly appeared very "downcast". A nervous breakdown, eh? Now that was something highly mysterious, something only to be talked about in hushed, uncertain tones. Maiden ladies of a particular age seemed most prone to attacks. It was very odd. But then women as a bunch were very odd. Was there a woman alive, Jim wondered, who was not terrified of silence? Later he used to wonder why girls turned quickly to see if their stocking seams were straight before diving into an air raid shelter. Yes, very odd.

But two days later 'brokendown' and 'downcast' were together again. Jolly good. Too good in fact to last. All too soon the foursome of Julie and Ken, Mary and Jim – after church and after Guides, became a threesome, Ken having gone AWOL.

Under Jim's interrogation Ken could only offer unconvincing excuses – "swotting for exams." Oh yeah? What in – monkey running? "Ken came and made a lame excuse about having a septic heel." Punning had become like a law of Nature – his dad's nature and now his: "Then went collecting signatures for a peace petition," as if any such puny Quaker efforts would check, in the slightest degree, Adolf's and Musso's maniacal ambitions.

But what to do about the immediate problem – jittery Julie?

Putting it bluntly, on Sunday evenings after church, when Mary and Jim just longed to be on their own, it became a pain in the neck to have Julie sometimes tagging along. Chivalry being what it was at the time (that Guild debate had amply confirmed its status, even in radical circles) Jim felt he couldn't just leave Julie without a male escort, straight after the service, on such a wild, dark January night. So he took both girls for a creepy, stumbling walk round the deeply shadowed churchyard, eerie rustles amid the sinister tangled ivy, moaning, skeletal tree branches swaying above. The ruse worked. Julie, possibly nervier than ever, went straight home – alone. Mary and Jim contentedly warmed themselves by a night-watchman's cheery brazier, preparatory to their goodnight kiss. (That arctic fumble had left its mark.)

"Did you do that on purpose?"

"What?"

"Suggesting a walk round the churchyard hoping to scare Julie off."

"Well, to be honest, I'm not too sure myself. Just instinct maybe. Anyway, it worked."

"I was a bit scared as well you know. It was rather spooky, especially where some of the gravestones were leaning at a funny angle." Mary gave a mock shiver.

"Maybe those ghosts had got out of the wrong side of the – coffin."

"Don't talk like that – please. It isn't right to mock the dead."

"Sorry."

"OK It is parky though."

Mary gave a real shiver and snuggled closer to Jim. They both edged a little nearer the red hot coals of the brazier.

So, finito – for the Julie problem.

*

The red hot poker problem was of quite a different order and had nothing to do with card playing or the planting of herbaceous borders.

"Boys, who among you are interested in pyrography?"

The sixth form students of History, seated in the small library, turned blank faces to the Deputy Head Master (who had now wakened from his doze) – and said nothing.

"Boys, who is or who are the pyromaniac or maniacs?"

'Simla' stared bleakly over his pince-nez at the half dozen or so lads sitting along one side of the heavy oak table. His large, shiny pink, bald head glinted under the electric light. Such thick headed sixth formers these – so wooden. But some had begun to look a little shame faced for they sensed the drift of these searing questions, spoken softly, with silky menace, in a lilting Welsh voice.

"Boys, who made this hole?"

Mr Owen stabbed a bony forefinger at what appeared to be an inkblot staining the table. It was indeed an inkblot as Jim well knew, for he had dabbed it there, on top of a cork which served to plug the hole burned through the table top with a red hot poker. Jim, if he hadn't started the pyrography, had certainly finished it.

"What a smoke."

His attempt at camouflage had failed dismally. All six conspiratorial arsonists (including the head prefect) owned up and were promptly wheeled before the Head for due punishment. No excuse could be offered, for the vandalism was inexcusable. No enquiries were made into home circumstances. By definition, a grammar bug had been properly brought up.

No satisfactory explanation could be advanced for the hole boring. Was Freud in some ways to blame? He often seemed to be. Chaucer perhaps, with his *Miller's Tale*? Possibly. It seemed more likely though that what one boy had started for a lark, during private study periods – heating the poker in the library's open fire, had been continued, on the emulation principle, by his peers. Anyway, not one of the six would split on the originator.

And the upshot? Chaos and confusion. With six prefects being stripped of their office of authority as punishment, rowdy elements in the school, and plenty existed, took the opportunity to become even rowdier.

"Head gave the school a lecture on general bad conduct of the place. Snow adds to general disorder. Other prefects harassed."

While Jim felt uncomfortable about the higher incidence of pandemonium for which he was partly to blame, his main worry was that his mom shouldn't find out about his criminal tendencies. He fretted too about the possible cost of repairs to the table. After four days, the "Descendum cum pocere in Tablum" six had their gowns of office restored. Peace, unlike the poker, did not descend but rowdiness was reduced and held at its normal level of the noisily boisterous.

Ah well, there might soon be weightier matters to worry about than red hot pokers and inky corks.

*

"Read the news Dad? Some Londoners are going to get air raid shelters. It says here that shelters will be provided free to families with incomes of less than two hundred and fifty pounds a year. At that rate we should get a buckshee one when it's our turn, shouldn't we?"

The question was put in a tentative tone, for Wilf always became rather defensive whenever family budgetary matters seemed likely to come up for discussion. His answer was evasive.

"Well, I'm damned sure I wouldn't pay for one."

"It goes on to say that the shelters need to be partly sunk in the ground – and that they measure six foot six by four foot six. That means we have enough room in the back garden for one."

Wilf growled an unintelligible reply which signified that 'a bear with a sore head' mood could be gaining the ascendancy. Jim thought it best to drop ARP matters – for the time being.

He steered his thoughts back to running. It would soon be time for the cross country race again. He began training. During the past twelve months, he had grown a little taller – to 5' 6½". That half inch made a world of difference for it meant that he was now nearer six foot than five. He had also broadened out.

It seemed prudent therefore, to drop the practice of running on the spot in the back kitchen, where a sudden slip against the oven door handle, or the solid edges of the mangle, might irreparably ruin all sorts of possible future opportunities on and off the running track and ploughed fields. And he made a firm resolution to steer well clear of any fish that seemed in the least bit 'iffy'.

So lots of steady running and short sprints around the school fields and over the springy turf of Perry Playing Fields – with Naylor, Doug and Evans. Jim made a prediction; "Naylor will win again easily this year. Marvellous runner."

Even so, Jim felt in good nick – he was meeting Mary regularly and they went "jolly good walks" together. Jim decided, with no tremor of misgiving, to disregard the austere regime he understood was practised by some athletes – i.e. forsaking the company of ladies during the later stages of training. In fact, for some weeks now, his diary entries had been starred with asterisks; coded kisses. This highly agreeable 'keep fit' programme of walks, talks, cuddles and kisses induced a blissfully happy frame of mind – jolted just occasionally by the brutalities of foreign affairs.

*

"Oh Norton, I'd like a word with you."

"Sir?"

Mr Williams, the new History teacher and initiator of the new discussion group, 'The Forum' went on,

"I'm organising a debate shortly in the Forum. It will be about the Spanish Civil War and our Government's recognition of General Franco's Government. Would you be prepared to present the viewpoint of *The Daily Worker* – using excerpts from the paper itself?"

"With pleasure sir." And Jim meant it.

He set to work with a will, for he was right behind the notion that an elected government should not be overthrown by a barbaric Fascist movement which drew on the support of ruthless German dive bombers and rich, powerful Nazi sympathisers in the West.

Other, strong or mealy mouthed viewpoints on the emotive issue of the Spanish Civil War, were stated by some of his sixth form pals.

Doug Baker, a highly intelligent lad, with a large, well shaped head, fair haired, excitable, put the case for *The Times*. Dave (being still a fifth former) spoke for *The Daily Herald* and Syd Whitley for *The Daily Telegraph*. *The Birmingham Post*, a respected national daily "called on" Dandy Sandy, and one of the Jackson twins represented the liberal *News Chronicle*. Jim Norton rooted and ranted for the Communist rag.

The official report of this clash of the minnows, in *The Bridge* (the school journal) contrasted the "strictly pro-Government and traditionally Conservative *Times*, with its calm, carefully weighed pontifical pronouncements and its impeccable English, and the Communistic organ...with its shock-tactics, its propaganda, its gruesome details, and its lurid description."

Jim had rather enjoyed presenting the 'gruesome' and the 'lurid' gory accounts and descriptions which were received with wild enthusiasm by the blood thirsty 'many headed' in the audience. Even so, he genuinely believed that the 'bloated capitalist' supporters of Franco deserved to be shocked. That Basque painter-chappy, Picasso, had rightly stirred things up after the Guernica atrocity, so why shouldn't he, Jim, in his small way, 'have a go' at those who were so complacently ready to ignore or condone the vicious brutalities of Fascism.

Emotions ran high and even after the debate had finished, an HGS civil war continued as – "a dust up in form room."

Jim also genuinely believed that the pacifist position, though praiseworthy in some ways, was overly idealistic and misconceived. Could pacifism exist, he wondered, if non-pacifists were not prepared to fight for and maintain a society in which pacifism was allowed? At the Guild he assessed one Quaker speaker as talking "a lot of blather about peace", and subsequently seconded the opposition to a motion stating that: 'Britain's re-armament cannot maintain peace.' Among his prepared notes appeared:

"The only way to stop dictators...is by offering a firm resistance. This can only be done by building up our navy, army and air force until they are so powerful that fascist powers dare not interfere with our possessions or liberties..."

He felt that such a crisp, logical approach was unassailable – but the motion was still carried, due to the 'biased audience' – a 'firebrand's' judgement.

*

"There you are, I told you the greedy bugger would."

There was no hint of 'I told you so' triumph in Wilf's voice.

"Who would what? And please moderate your language."

"That bloody sod – Hitler. He's invaded Czechoslovakia now. I told you the Munich Agreement wouldn't last. Not worth the paper it was written on. Fat lot of good it has done us."

"Well," said Jim, "I suppose it gave us a bit of a breather to build up our armaments and get ready for war."

"I grant you that – but Hitler's factories won't have been idle either, and they've had a massive start on us. No, Chamberlain isn't the man to stand up to a thug like Hitler. And the French aren't much cop either. Too many of their big bugs are Nazi sympathisers. We need someone like Uncle Joe on our side. You can't keep giving way to a bullying bastard like Hitler."

"Language, Wilf, language."

Whatever the colour of the language, Jim believed his dad to be right. But his mother had a point as well;

"All this talk of war is horrible. It makes you wonder why mothers bother to raise sons. Too many fine boys were lost in the Great War."

"Well, you're right enough there."

Jim's parents fell silent – one probably thinking of a dead son and the other of a dead lover.

To try and lighten the sombre mood, Jim picked up an old comic. "What do you think of this Pop?"

He read out:

" "Things you never see

The key for an elephant's trunk

A patch for a cloudburst

A nut for a thunderbolt

A hat on the head of a brush

Knees for the legs of a table." " "

Jim's mother gave a wan smile.

"Aren't you cutting it rather fine, dear, for your date with Mary?"

"Crikey, you're right."

Within seconds he was steadily loping his way towards Handsworth Wood.

Two days to go to the 'Big Run'.

"A balloon for part of balloon barrage up this dinnertime. Saw Mary after Guides. Cold so we sheltered in a new house. Last training.*"

Then the eve of the 1939 race.

"You said you had something for me."

"Yes, but you can't have it now."

"Why not?"

"You just can't that's all."

Mary wasn't going to budge, Jim could sense that. He sheathed both rapier and broadsword of his 'wit' – so leaving unscathed his pre-race conditioning. "... had a lovely time.* It gets better."

On the morning of the cross country race enter Dickie – promoted from messenger to special courier in recognition of his weighty services that day. For he brought with him from his 'soppy sister' (he narrowly escaped demotion and decapitation at that point) – a note, containing words of affectionate encouragement *and* a "...mascot. It was the one she wouldn't give me last night. A little pixie."

Such attentiveness lifted Jim's heart, but he still suffered agonising cramp and only "managed to struggle in fourth"; the worst position of all – just out of the medals. Still, there might be another chance next year – at age 16 – and maybe 5' 7" tall.

Yes, soon it would be his birthday, another milestone passed. What was that old saying? Ah yes: 'sweet sixteen and never been kissed'. He recalled that Mary had once pronounced him "sweet". Last Christmas it was, when he had given her that ½lb of Black Magic chocs. But as for the 'never been kissed' – what a wonderful nonsense of a description in his case! Better not become too smug, though. Life had a tendency to move on. It would be a sensible move to set another training programme in motion – one for ballroom dancing. Then he might eventually be able to really sweep his girl off her feet to;

"Sweet and lovely
Sweeter than the roses in May
And she loves me
Is there any more I can say?"

'Roses in May? A bit early, surely? Poetic licence no doubt; and better than June in the rhyming circumstances. But stick to the point Jim lad,' he murmured to himself.

Being able to dance well appeared to offer far more hope for deepening romance than the clodhopper state. Girls seemed to go so soft and dreamy, so moony if their fellers could dance with flair and confidence.

"When she nestles in my arms so tenderly..."

But how to make a start? Once more, good old private study periods came to the rescue.

"Copied instructions for dancing from a book with Dandy and practised steps" – chalked out on the floor of the sixth form room. "Had some fun." But little progress was made by leader or led. Too much doubling up laughter for that. Try again – from the beginning.

"Saw Mary and Irene and we went to Guild Dance. Had a great, spiffing glorious time. Think I have got the hang of dancing now. Good bit of fun. Mary had had some new shoes today. Bit knocked about now."

Small wonder. Jim's feet and legs still seemed better co-ordinated for a rugged tackle, quick sprint or steady lope. Would it help, he wondered, if he Brilliantined his hair?

He couldn't help but notice that chaps with dark sleek hair, who danced a sinuous tango had great success in 'pulling the birds'– and a plentiful, changing supply at that. No, it was too much to ask– was the Brilliantine treatment. Once he had experimented for two whole days with that perfumed goo from its shiny, round and golden tin. But he had been a mere oafish boy at the time, in Remove C, when he had fashioned his hair into greasy spikes only for them to fall, to be re-fashioned and fall again, as he gazed moodily from his seat by the window across to the dreary secondary school opposite.

No, he wasn't really a Brilliantine person, and anyway, he had a great girlfriend who didn't moan about the state of her new shoes, now brutally scuffed by his yokel like, raw recruit attempts at a Military Two-Step.

And there she was, an uncomplaining sweetheart, sitting snugly by his side, in the park shelter as the rain poured steadily down. Just the two of them – no one else about – as they held hands. It was Jim's sixteenth birthday. Gosh, he did feel a lot older than 'this time last year' – and vastly more pleased with life. Sixth form studies and a great tomboy girlfriend had wonderfully enriched his intellectual and emotional experiences.

"Penny for them?"

Jim's face coloured just sufficiently to arouse Mary's curiosity.

"No, I don't think I can tell you, not at that price."

"Tuppence then..."

"And a kiss?"

"Trust you."

They kissed. The tuppence payment was waived.

"It's only what happened a few days ago. Here, I'll read out what I've written in my diary."

""Had to act as model for Derek Shaw's Art Exam for three hours. Had rests. Would have earned 15/- if it had been for an artist. Quite an experience.""

"I'll bet it was. Tell me, weren't you cold?"

"Why should I have been cold?"

"Silly, you know why," Mary paused, "models often have to pose in" – another pause – "birthday suits."

"Saucy minx. You're wrong in my case. Derek had to sketch a head and shoulders portrait."

"How did you manage to keep still, all that time?"

"I put it down to all the hours I had sat, as a small boy, on my Gran's horsehair sofa, squashed in place by a row of old fogies."

"Now tell me what you've written in your diary for last Saturday when we went to see *Cinderella*."

Jim took a quick glance at the entry for 1st April and quickly closed the diary. He edged a little further from Mary's side.

"No, sorry, I can't do that. You'd get a swelled head if I did. And you've told me, more than once, that you can never get a hat to suit you."

With her free hand Mary made a fist and punched Jim on the knee.

"Oh, go on, be a sport."

"No - or in the words of the song: "No, No a Thousand Times No!""

"Misery."

"I can tell you that at night I sorted some cigarette cards."

"Get away. Tell me more."

"No fear."

"One of these days young Jim, I shall pinch that diary of yours and have a good read."

"I don't think so."

"And what will you be writing this evening about the tie I've just bought you for your birthday?"

"Oh, I dare say I'll think of something," Jim said airily.

He made a mental note never to mention that last Christmas he had received not one but two ties from Babbacombe Brenda.

Mary's present was a real Tootall tie, with light grey and dark blue stripes - very smart.

*

"If there's a gleam in her eye,
Each time she straightens your tie,
You know the lady's in love ..."

Jim didn't trust himself to think the unthinkable - Mary was only 14½ - and yet, and yet;

"If she gets dressed for a date
Without that waiting you hate,
You know..."

Well, there'd been no difficulty so far - and Mary did look a treat in that "blue swagger coat". On one occasion, due to a misunderstanding, she had even waited for *him* - a full half hour, or was it an hour even?

Jim cut short his reflections. Live for the day, that was the ticket. And the day was 5th April. Even the Government had given the day a nod of recognition, for it had then announced its plans for the mass evacuation of children should war break out. Mary herself was becoming an "evacuee", going away for a week's holiday at Easter with her parents.

Absence would certainly make his heart grow fonder. Jim knew that – but it would also provide opportunities to try something new. So, "... painted bench in garden. Rain spoilt it." Still trouble with his timing. Learning to row on the park pool: "Dave laughed his eye out." Jim's timing still at fault. At times of temporary set backs such as these, Jim took comfort from what *The Bridge* football reporter had written;

"The 2nd XI's record is better" (than the 1st XI's).

"Norton and Jones play a steady, forceful game in the defence."

Jim liked that – 'steady and forceful' eh. He'd show 'em!

Chapter Eight

Hey Nonino

"Hell's bells! These journalists do write some tripe."

Jim kicked his heels in vexation against the wooden boards of the boxed in lavatory pan. He was seated in his quiet reading room, (along the narrow, uneven blue-bricked yard) – a white washed cubicle of privacy flanked by the coal-house, on one side and the glory hole of junk and garden tools on the other.

Really, he thought to himself, some of these scribblers are a real pain – he grinned – in the backside.

From an early age, Jim had been strongly urged to be sceptical about what he read in newspapers, most especially Tory rags. Now, he was irritated by the account given of Birmingham's rent strike. Well, be fair, perhaps not so much cross about the account itself, as the fact that he couldn't find the rest of the contentious article. That was sometimes the trouble with ripping up 'old' newspapers into rough squares, spiking them on a bent nail in the wall to serve, as what he understood to be called, among the middle class – toilet paper.

Apparently, rent collectors on council house estates had run into protests from tenants and refusals to pay increased rents, in areas such as Kingstanding. One unfortunate collector had even been forced to escape on his bicycle from tenants' wrathful attentions. Ted, Jim's very politically aware brother, and a Kingstanding council house tenant himself, would give the family the 'real low-down', on his next visit. As a convinced left wing Socialist, Ted was also sure to be very hot under the collar about the Government's recently announced plans for conscription. 'Call-up' would start sometime in June.

Jim stood up and flushed the lavatory, grinning as he did so, for he had just remembered Dave's Confucius joke.

"Confucius he s'lay: 'swinging chain sign of warm seat'." Such practical wisdom. Dashed clever, those Chinese.

With the typical self absorption of youth, Jim was far less concerned about local rent strikes and national call-ups, than about what might happen today, 6th May – the HGS Sports Day. His eagerness to do well had prompted him to train hard, to over-train perhaps, for his thigh muscles seemed far too taut and had given him some gyp in practising for the long jump – the crucial event.

He knew he was expected to do well – but so were others, his old pal Doug Baker for one, and most especially 'Speedy' Broadhurst. Boys could enter three events but the long jump was the only one in which Speedy and Jim were to clash. Much would depend on the result. The long jump was to be held before the 100 and 220 yard sprints, which Broadhurst was widely expected to win. Jim had entered for the later programmed quarter and the mile.

With Jimmy Lester (of the 'Big Run') in mind, Jimmy Norton sprinted hard for the takeoff board. He knew this third and last jump was his best – but was it good enough?

He waited, heart palpitating, near the sand pit.

The two masters who were acting as judges, carefully measured and re-measured the leap (it seemed to take an age) conferred briefly, and then announced that – Norton was the winner with a jump of 17' 1½". Whew! He had won – by just ½"! All he had to do now was win the quarter – and the mile.

Although he did feel for Speedy, such 'hard cheese' losing by a mere ½", Jim was sufficiently fired up by his narrow victory to win the quarter reasonably comfortably, even though the thigh trouble was still, well, troublesome.

Everything now depended on the final event of the day, for, as anticipated, Speedy had won both sprints.

It was perfect weather for running the mile – bright blue sky, the peerless blue of early Spring, warm and sunny atmosphere, little breeze, and, what a bonus! an excited, supportive girlfriend, her parents and brothers too, among the sizeable, animated crowd.

The track wasn't so hot though – four laps at a pace needed to win, would be testing on the well cut, but uneven turf, with a distinct slope on the bends downhill into the back straight, and what naturally appeared to be far steeper slopes uphill, on the bends leading to the home straight before the pavilion. Still, it was the same for all the runners, Jim reminded himself, including Doug and Lofty – both strong threats.

The starting pistol cracked. Jim sprinted to the front. That impulsive streak in his nature made him a natural front runner. At the bell he still led, grimacing with pain from his knotted thigh muscles. Coming into the home straight he heard through confused senses, what, for the performer, is the sweetest of music – applause and warm hearted cheering steadily swelling in volume.

"Come on Jim, come on! Come on Norton! Come on lad, come on!"

He breasted the tape – senior athletics champion for 1939 – a dream fulfilled. Yippee!

He had been told, though he wasn't sure whether to believe it, that he was the first sixth former ever to win the Senior Championship. He wasn't going to check – that would smack of conceit. It was enough that with great and glowing pride he could walk, with his mom, down Wood Lane, towards home, bearing the large, handsome, silver plated cup on which his name was later to be engraved on a small shield, alongside doughty champions of the past.

A pity though that his dad had not turned up. He wondered why. Wilf hadn't volunteered any explanation for his absence. Jim had to assume that Pop had his own good or disputable reasons for failing to cheer his son on. But Jim didn't like to ask what they might be, for fear of perhaps being snubbed – brusquely at that. But he couldn't help seeking, in his own thoughts, an answer partially satisfactory to himself, while remaining charitable to his father.

Was it anything to do with his Dad's gammy leg? With the fact that for years now, his Dad had been cruelly robbed of his own favourite outdoor activity – cycling? Or perhaps Sports Day, and Jim's own success, formed too poignant a reminder of what John had achieved on the running track, and of the potential that had been snuffed out in bloody Flanders?

No good brooding about it. Look on the bright side. That splendid trophy, already looking totally at home on top of the roll-top desk, could be metaphorically waved in triumph under the acidulous noses of the 'will Sal rear him' brigade. And yes, also under the inflamed conk of that bullying master who had once so humiliated him in class, by comparing him with the limp lettuce that he brought to school with his cheese and tomato sandwiches.

On the balmy, warm evening of that 'best of days', Mary and Jim celebrated success by going to the pictures, to the Regal, a rather plush cinema on the Soho Road side of Handsworth; "1/3 seats". Wowee! Two, one and threes, equals a half dollar, a sizeable coin and no mistake. It was a good job, that next day, over the tinned salmon and vinegar, Uncle Les, generous as ever, "doubled pocket money for next three weeks" – in recognition of his nephew's triumph.

Quite a leg up that, in the social scale, to sit in the circle at the Regal, among much older courting couples, some of whom looked sniffily, others curiously or indulgently at such youngsters in their amorous midst.

Robert Donat played his part splendidly in *The Citadel*. Jim vaguely wondered how many of those present had kept their eyes on the screen *all* through the drama. Not that it mattered.

During the interval Jim fetched tubs of ice cream and stumbled as he returned to join Mary. He knew this wasn't really due to the swelter of a crowded Saturday night audience, the excitement and exertions of the day – but worsening short sightedness. How much longer could he continue to disguise the reality of his condition? And why was he so wretchedly sensitive about the probability of wearing glasses? It wasn't as though he was even in the same league as Robert Donat as far as masculine good looks went. He'd think about the problem again when he was less tired.

A few days later, another jolt, of a different sort, to set him thinking again. At the Inter-School Sports held at the Alexander Ground, home of top-notch Birchfield Harriers, he failed to qualify for the finals of the quarter or the mile, "chaps miles too big for me. Veritable giants...still...I shall be here next year, and praps do better," being a little taller (a quarter inch maybe) a few pounds heavier, and definitely stronger – always assuming war had not broken out and put the kybosh on decent grub.

As for the 'building up of Jim' programme, beaten egg whisked in sherry might need to feature – not just the once, as on the morning of May 6th 1939, but twice, maybe even three times in the Spring of 1940. The problem, naturally, was not teetotalism or the price of eggs but the price of sherry, even of the cheapest brand.

The school's spanking new gym, just opened, could also play a most valuable muscle building part. Light, clean, airy, and splendidly equipped, the gym, in fact was "a really super place. Glad I am stopping on next year if it's just for this."

Although he sensed tension in the air at home, along with the luscious, lingering odours of bubble and squeak, he knew next to nothing definite of the arguments going on within the 'kitchen Cabinet' about whether 'my son' should continue at the Grammar, or 'he's my son as well', should go to work.

For Jim, the month of May and much of June were wonderfully idyllic.

"Bliss was it in that dawn to be alive,
But to be young was very heaven."

Wordsworth had been exulting about the early, idealistic days of the French Revolution – but his words seemed just as apposite to the budding, near blossoming romance of Mary and Jim.

Shakespeare's lines were even better.

"Then come kiss me, sweet and twenty:
Youth's a stuff will not endure."

It was a great comfort to Jim to know that, like himself, England's greatest poet counted kisses – for "twenty" did not refer to age. But at sixteen, Jim did not get beyond "at least seven times." Still, it was a learning process – and the restraining conventions of the day remained widespread and powerful.

For instance, the sign of the 'twitching curtain' signified a major inhibiting force which worked maliciously, malevolently, spitefully, against the tremulous yearnings of young lovers, especially the very youthful ones aged fourteen and sixteen.

Twitch – 'Well who would have thought it? Here Else, take a peep.'

Twitch – 'Well I never, she can't be much above fourteen and she comes from such a nice respectable family.'

Twitch – 'Now they're saying goodnight'; (sharp indrawn breath) 'Great heavens! She's kissing him back, the hussy! And not just a peck either from the look of it. I don't know what young girls are coming to these days, I really don't. Their grandmothers must be spinning in their graves. Think we should have a quiet word with her mother?'

Twitchers apart, both youngsters remained well aware of the need for skilful discretion rather than brazen display. No kiss because – "...lady at bus stop." "...too many people about"; "Wouldn't let me kiss her cause we were just at the top of her road"; "moved our 'au revoir' spot to..."(classified).

As for the learning process, this was champagne sparkling delightful – despite some disappointments.

Disappointments could arise from a variety of causes, one of which appeared beyond all human control – the all too common, common cold. Jim associated the winter months with a space by the mangle which seemed to be permanently occupied by a white enamel pail, full to the brim with 'dirty' handkerchiefs in soak. So, if Jim had a cold, he would not attempt to kiss Mary. If Mary had a cold, but it wasn't pink and sniffy nose obvious, then Mary would still plainly signal 'lips off tonight laddy'. When both had a cold – misery. When neither – *bliss*.

Other kissing inhibitors derived from human frailty, Jim's mostly. Inherent shyness: "...couldn't find enough courage." Lamentable lack of perception: (a signal not recognised or understood too late). "She gave me opportunity...must have been daft", to let the chance slip.

But improvements came with the better weather and the clearer recognition of the significant unstated – "kissed her twice: still she more or less worked it." Champagne sparkling indeed.

At the end of 1939 the diary listed thirty-three notable dates for the year. 3rd September, for example -"war broke out" – no prizes for guessing that one. But 14th May "epic event"? Just three days earlier, Chamberlain had warned Hitler that a German invasion of Danzig would mean war. 14th May – no connection with that steely warning but a warm and thrilling invitation. Not a 'hands off' situation – rather a 'hands on'.

"We went into our usual house. Epic event. She stood looking at me from one corner of room. Compelled me to go over and kiss her. What a thrill."

It was those eyes of course, those large, expressive, golden hazel eyes. Adjusted to full allure, they engulfed a chap. They assuredly did – even in a partly built house, with bricks, cement, plaster, strewn about the floorboards.

Jim was blissful enough with the prevailing kissing pattern but realised that kissing was but a stage on a journey of discovery. But what was the next stage and when might it be properly taken? He was not in too much of a hurry, even with almost certain war approaching, but it would be nice to have a good general idea.

Yes, it really would, particularly now that Mary occasionally wrote to him in such excitingly endearing terms. Of course, she might sometimes have had a giggling school pal at her side to egg her on. But no matter, there was no mistaking the warmth in the terms or tone of her notes. Take that recent billet très doux Dickie had brought. In it Mary had written "dearest darling Jim". Of course, the minx wanted something from him – but such disarming, charming tricks were only to be expected when you started going out with girls. "...she wanted to go to Villa Cross and see *You can't take it with You*... seemed a shame to go to pictures, but we had a grand time."

Jim always preferred to be outdoors whenever the weather was fine – girl or no girl for company, but given such warm endearments, he naturally gave way.

But he really did enjoy the Oscar-winning film. Great fun, the interplay between level-headed and zany characters as portrayed by a 'star studded' cast, headed by Jean Arthur, Ann Miller, James Stewart, Lionel Barrymore.

A few days later another, far more difficult choice had to be made – a choice with no romantic associations whatsoever. The dilemma found curious expression in Jim's diary.

"Undecided whether to go to Sunday School outing or to town and sell lifeboats."

These seemed strange matters to be weighed one against the other – but both were arranged to take place the following Saturday. And, naturally, it wasn't a case of selling 'real life' lifeboats but paper flags in support of the R.N.L.I.

The entry continued even more curiously:

"'Budge says the devil. Budge not, says my conscience. Fiend, you counsel well. Conscience, you counsel well.' Think conscience will win."

End of diary entry.

*

Jim felt he had now grown out of Sunday School outings. They weren't much bottle – kids' stuff really, even the swanking about on the back seat of the coach. Supporting the R.N.L.I. was a worthy cause and selling flags on their behalf would be an entirely new experience. And that's what it proved to be.

"June 10 Saturday...Cut the last period so that I could get home early and change, so as to be in town for two o'clock. Sold lifeboat flags all afternoon till five o'clock. Did quite well. Had some amusing arguments. Snubbed hundreds of times, chiefly by made up females, dressed in the height of fashion. Went in Milk Bar in Colmore Row. Spent 10d on refreshments. Saw Mom. Went to Lewis's. Had a cycling jacket for holidays. Mom lost her purse but found it again luckily. Fetched [bird] seed from Perry Barr at night for Uncle Les."

"Little man you've had a busy day," went the song.

'Phew – not arf,' – echoed Jim in his drowsy thoughts.

But what about this 'budge says the devil? Budge not says my conscience'?

Would such 'guidance' help him in his search for knowledge about the dating-mating game? He didn't quite see how. He was only too well aware of the sensitivity of his conscience – just think back a minute to the Onion Fair of last October. Because he had promised his mom not to be late home, he had almost certainly missed his first realistic chance for "Oh, that kiss": at Mary's home into the bargain, long before 4th January 1939. From that incident, and many others from his childhood, he remained fairly confident that his conscience would not budge by an alarming amount or in a truly perilous, perdition bound, direction.

But as to the devil, the formidable fiend, that was a much more tricky business. Fiends came in all shapes, sizes and disguises. Back in 1934, even 1935, as an unassertive small boy, in short trousers and matching scabby knees, he evaluated several of the masters as veritable fiends, and one particular bullying teacher as an arch fiend – with knobs on. Jim acknowledged to himself that, on occasion, he himself could display a 'devil of a temper'. But usually the angry outbursts only came when he felt that he, or someone close to him, had been unjustly treated.

This kind of introspection was rapidly getting him nowhere, he thought. What he really needed was skilfully and sensitively presented guidance on the art and etiquette of courtship.

But where on earth from? He thought it unlikely that he would find a 'copy' alongside *Flying Aces* at Woolworths. Such delicate and highly personal matters could not possibly be discussed with Mom or Dad – or even carefree bachelor uncles. Smutty talk at school, in some ways graphically instructive (especially some of the 'poetry' readings, principally and appropriately in the lavatories) still left him confused – not about physical functions, but personal relationships.

He had consistently been brought up, not to place women on a pedestal, but to treat them always with courtesy, consideration and respect. He knew vaguely that dreadful things could happen to lads who did, or attempted to do, dreadful things to girls who were 'under age'. Oh, well, he supposed things would sort themselves out eventually. Or would they? Girls could be such teases.

Should he have a chat with Bill, an unconventional chap. He'd proved it, definitely proved it, having stayed contentedly married to Jim's sister.

Jim smiled inwardly at his recollections of his brother-in-law, especially at those from the good old Crompton Road days. When first courting May, Bill had worn brown boots with his Sunday best, navy blue suit – as hideous a gaffe as could be, if you belonged to the respectable sector of the working class.

"Brahn boots, I arsks yer, brahn boots..."

Dear old Bill, of the receding hairline, beaky nose and golden hearted disposition. A willing slave was Bill to his pert, pretty and wilful wife. He grumbled, he blasphemed, he protested – all in good natured vein – and obeyed.

Jim, in his imagination, could hear him still, shuffling down the long, draughty hall from the front room, on his regular mission to fill the coal scuttle at the outdoors coalhouse which was open to the elements – often unkind elements when coal was needed.

"Marta, rambling rose of the wild wood..."

ending with a parodied last line:

"With a dewdrop on your nose de-e-e-e-vine!"

In those days Bill had still employed his own nose in a rather curious fashion. Any object he picked up – a cushion, a book, a newspaper, an orange – he would sniff at – at very close range. Even after that side-splitting (for Jim) day when Bill cauterised his conk by piercing the skin of a hot rice pudding, he wasn't entirely cured of the habit.

On one of his many return trips to the front room (May and Bill's temporary home) Bill had stopped, for a moment, in the kitchen/living room – with its heavy cast iron range, a table, and a Jim doing his homework, a modest bowl of fruit by his elbow.

Bill had picked up a lemon, sniffed it and then placed it between the glass pane and fine net curtain of the sash window. The effect was startling – for there, delicately cradled in its gentle mesh support, snuggled a small, firm breast with a large, rigid and pointed nipple. Bill artfully jiggled the lemon, chuckled and went on his way, singing,

""When I grow too old to dream,
I'll have you to remember...""

*

Then there was May – could she help? She had once, indirectly. The memory brought a faint blush to Jim's cheek, now really clean shaven since his Mom had bought him a "super shaving set in zip case with every toilet accessory" for his sixteenth birthday.

Yes, May his half-sister, now a bonny mother with a bonny son, 'Young Bill', but then – he blushed again.

One evening in her courting days, May of the tip-tilted nose, winsome appearance and sharp wit, had burst into the kitchen, seized Jim by the hands and showed him how a girl should be held when dancing. Jim was spun around in a clumsy twirl or two. Nothing wrong with that – a high spirited, happy girl sharing her exuberance with an awkward, diffident schoolboy brother, who was fair game for unmalicious teasing.

Only one snag if that was the word. While the schoolboy was fully dressed, May flounced about in flimsy, softly clinging, pale peach-coloured underwear. Satisfied that her saucy magic had worked, she waltzed off leaving the schoolboy flushed, embarrassed – but not really regretting the experience.

No, on reflection, he wouldn't be able to consult May and Bill, even though he went to their home regularly for a bath. How on earth would he broach such a subject?

Whatever he tried, he knew he would blush and stutter. He would be woefully unequal to the inevitable leg pulling available to an experienced married couple. Besides, such chat and backchat as might arise, would be unfair and unkind, in his romantic view, to his girlfriend. He shrank from the prospect of having 'love's young dream' sullied in any way, by possibly coarse – at least by implication, comments.

Perhaps it would be better to let matters take their natural course – and anyway, even from his limited experience, girls seemed to know far more about courting procedures, hanky panky, etiquette – call it what you would – than boys, especially where a mother took a close interest in a daughter's friendships. Jim decided to stay on the alert for encouraging signals.

Brushing troublesome but still interesting thoughts to one side, Jim began to hum a song;

"While strolling in the park one day,

In the merry month of May ..."

While it had not been May but September of last year when Mary and Jim had met – in the park, it was most decidedly the very merry month of May now. The high season of 'hey nonino' without a doubt.

Evening after evening, Mary and Jim spent their free time in the fresh, green-leafed outdoors. Without even discussing which way to go, they headed, evening after evening, towards the western fringes of Handsworth Wood. Once the newly built houses had been left behind, they held hands and wandered dreamily among the copses and open fields that sloped down towards the turbid River Tame.

Unfriendly 'Private' notices meant nothing in the youngsters' springtime glory world, and so were blithely disregarded. Around them enchanting drifts of delicately scented bluebells spread their hyacinth haze through dappled sunlight. A magical area, a magical time.

"I don't think it's right to pick bluebells."

"Oh, don't you now. And why not?"

"Well, my uncles say they don't last long once they've been picked. And besides, they look better in the wild."

"Are your uncles expert gardeners then?"

"Yes they are, as a matter of fact."

"They'd know about the birds and bees then?"

Mary's eyes sparkled mischievously.

"Er, well, er I suppose so."

Jim gulped – but struggled on.

"Uncle Harold does know his onions about butterflies, that I do know."

"Chump."

"Who, Uncle Harold? That's hardly fair."

"No you, you chump."

Mary strolled on, gracefully threading a way between slender birch trees. Jim followed – at a short distance.

Reaching a small glade, bathed in caressingly warm, early evening sunshine, Mary stooped, cleared away some twigs and withered leaves from the short grass, sat and then lay down and closed her eyes – an enigmatic smile on her lips.

In such a setting at such a time, Mary made an enchanting picture. Jim stood gazing with admiration and love at what for him, was the epitome of springtime loveliness.

Then he too lay down, on his side, close to Mary – his hands gently holding her firm young shoulders. Her smooth, bronzed arms moved lightly across his back. Jim kissed her – tenderly. Mary's response was warm, loving – a little dreamy.

Silence in the bluebell glade apart from an occasional faint rustle when a soft breeze gently swayed the leaves. A few drowsy insects, one or two bees perhaps among them, hummed on their darting ways.

A lingering kiss – a firm but tender embrace – and silence for a wonderful while.

"Jim."

Mary had opened her glowing, golden hazel eyes.

"Mm."

"I think it's about time to go home."

The light brown hazel eyes looked troubled. Jim sighed – a sigh of resignation to frustrating fate.

Mary gently pushed Jim away from her, looking at her wrist watch as she did so.

"Yes, it's time."

"Yes, I suppose you're right."

Mary sat up and extended an arm to Jim, now standing, who pulled her to her feet. Mary carefully began smoothing the creases out of that enchantingly pretty summer dress, light blue in colour with a white daisy pattern – that appealed to him so much.

"Better not go home with bits of grass in my hair." Mary giggled. "No grass stains on my dress I hope?"

"Turn round then. No, you're in the clear."

"Good. Now lend me your comb then please."

"Not until you've given me one more kiss."

"What a cheek. Tell you what. You can have another kiss if you let me have a look at that precious diary of yours."

"Sorry, nobody sees that but me."

"Well, we'll see about that."

With a tigress like pounce, Mary plunged her left hand into Jim's right hand jacket pocket (she knew well enough where 'that blinkin' diary' was kept). Simultaneously, her right hand made for Jim's left hand trouser pocket (she knew the whereabouts of the comb too). Taken a little off guard, Jim struggled to retain possession of much that he held dear in life. The tussle became more physical but the diary remained inviolate. Scarlet with exertion, excitement and near ecstasy, he had to cede the comb to his charmer. The beautiful Mona Lisa smile on Mary's face reminded him of that waltzing skirmish with his sister light years ago.

Mary finished combing her hair and shyly handed back the comb. Together, in silence, the youngsters wandered back through the now darker coloured drifts of bluebells, to the edge of the wood – and, dash it, semi-detached respectability. They paused in the last of the leafy shade, kissed briefly and silently walked back into a world bereft of bluebells.

Chapter Nine
Storm Clouds and War Clouds

Handsworth Park sported two sets of swings, adjacent to one another but sharply separated by a spiked, iron railing fence. The boys' swings could be identified by the two iron rings and trapeze bar, not supplied for the girls' swings in the interests of feminine decorum, which, in 1939, would be put perilously at risk if girls were allowed to circle, heels over head.

Invariably irascible park-keepers discouraged boys from drifting into the girls' playground, but the eye fluttering charmers usually lured some moths to the flame. Girls, however, did not sidle, let alone drift, into the boys' swings. Quite taboo.

Soon this entire area signified wretchedly miserable heartache for Jim. Only a few days after the longest day of the year (27th June), the evening of which had been thrillingly spent at "our usual secluded spot", Jim unexpectedly came across Mary during the dinner break – in the park.

"Horror of horrors. Saw Mary with two of our [HGS] kids."

Jim strove to be reasonable; "still I don't suppose it is her wish but her pals." Just as he might be trapped into a compromising situation, if ever he went with Ken again on one of Ken's 'expeditions.'

But two days later, there she was again, looking a treat in her gymslip – but not like his girl of the bluebell wood. This time she was in the company of "4 C louts on swings. Tried to hide behind her girlfriends. Went towards them. Came and spoke to me. Had to. Hope she only tried to hide so that I would not get the wrong impression. I'm afraid she takes too much for granted. There will be a big row one of these days. Make or break our friendship."

Hurt and bewildered, Jim tried to make sense of this sickening, solar plexus blow to his feelings, and of what, to his romantic nature, seemed like a betrayal. He recollected that just a few days ago, and a week only since 'the seven times a kissing' (at least), Mary had turned up late for a date "through sheer forgetfulness," – fishy that. And then there had been that recent 'dust up' at school. Even fishier.

As a prefect, Jim had been chivvying lads from out of the cloakroom so they would not be late for class. One boy, known by sight, but not name, stayed behind. With all the other boys gone, he turned to face Jim in an attitude of suppressed anger and defiance. Jim eyed him warily, wondering what was up.

"I wanted to talk to you."

"Oh, why?"

"You know Mary Leigh don't you?"

The question sounded more like an accusation and the questioner was obviously in a highly agitated state, glowering belligerently, clenching and unclenching his fists.

"Yes. So what of it?"

"She's a snipe you know."

A snipe? What did Jim know about a snipe? Only that it was a game bird of some sort, with a long bill. So what on earth was this indignant, fuming kid on about? Mary, with her tomboy nature, was certainly game for many unladylike adventures, as Jim well knew. But there was nothing wrong with her 'bill'; in fact, she had rather a charming nose. Heavens above, he, if anyone, should know, he had been close enough, often enough, to be quite sure. But he was wandering again.

"What was that you just said?"

"Mary Leigh is a snipe."

The incensed boy obviously intended an insult with the term. The right response? What might Harry Wharton, Jimmy Lester have done? WHACK!

Slightly to his own surprise, and to the boy's total consternation, Jim found that he had slapped the insulter hard on his right cheek. A scarlet patch flamed up on the boy's face. Nothing was said and the boy promptly left the cloakroom. Mary's reputation had been warmly defended.

*

Had Mary lost interest in him, Jim wondered? She had just claimed she couldn't see him for another ten days, yes, ten whole days, making a weekend Guides' camp one of her reasons.

Ten whole days. It just didn't add up. Had Mary really wanted to see him, as in the old days, she would certainly have found, or created, an opportunity within that period, to have arranged a date, probably via Dickie.

So, she didn't want to see him. So much seemed clear. Did that mean she wanted to see someone else? Murky waters there.

Mary was an attractive girl, popular at school and with no shortage of admirers from boys' schools. And not even Jim's mother would have claimed that Jim was good looking; a channel swimmer possibly, but no boyish Ronald Colman, Clark Gable or Errol Flynn. So Jim accepted that he might well have rivals.

The snipe fancier obviously knew things that Jim was unaware of. But if he began asking questions, however obliquely, about Mary's possible new interests, he felt sure that word would filter back to Mary, leaving him open to charges of mistrusting her – and so bring about, probably, the rupture he was so anxious to avoid. Hell! And to go and check to see if she really was at the Guides' camp, pitched at no great distance, would be demeaning. So, all in all, Jim felt himself to be in a right old fix.

But why didn't Mary want to see him, except at longer intervals, which might become even longer? Was this a feminine way of saying 'Take the hint big boy, I'm giving you the brush off'? Was being fickle one of a snipe's principal characteristics? Did Mary want to play the field? Had she become a little bit scared at their developing closeness? Questions, questions – always questions.

Jim's head knew well enough that he could make no claim on her – crikey! She wasn't yet fifteen. But this 'doesn't seem to care' attitude which had recently developed, he found deeply wounding. As was so often the case, Al Bowlly could crooningly summarise the situation.

> " "Is that the way to treat a sweetheart,
> Who's head over heels in love with you.
> You take the heart right out of sweetheart,
> By playing around with someone new.

If you say you don't care, we'll call it a day,
But don't be unfair in a roundabout way ..."""

- especially not on the girls' swings.

And it was not so bad for Al. He was well paid for singing about heartache, and was never short of lady admirers.

After a tetchy discussion, Mary agreed to travel with Jim to Elmdon for the official opening of Birmingham's airport – tickets free, courtesy of Uncle Les.

"Woke up to the sound of a terrific downpour of rain" – and that sound persisted for much of the day – "terrible conditions. Quagmire. Trousers practically ruined." Mary "looked lovely" at the journey's outset, but the diary, possibly chivalrously, made no mention of her bedraggled appearance at the end of the show. Still, Jim had enjoyed and admired the aerial displays put on by "Spitfires, Hurricanes, Blenheims, Skuas." Overall however, the wretched, dispiriting, drenching weather and the deep, cloying mud, hardly constituted the best basis for an 'all is forgiven' reconciliation. Relationships remained tense, the atmosphere – sullen and brooding.

Thursday (Thor's Day with a vengeance) 20th July.

"Had a row which had been threatening for weeks."

"Where the dickens have you been?"

"Playing tennis, can't you see?" – a careless wave of the racquet.

"With your posh new friends, at that posh new club, I suppose?"

"Don't be silly."

"You didn't tell me you were going to play tennis."

"Why should I? And in any case, I told Dickie where you would be and that he was to tell you where I was. Didn't he see you?"

"Yes, he did, but he didn't tell me you would be half an hour late."

"Well, I can't just break off from a game and say – 'excuse me, I'm going to meet a boyfriend, a bad tempered, impatient boyfriend.' Besides, I was enjoying the match." Mary's eyes sparked with anger and defiance.

"So, you'd rather please your stuck up new friends, than me."

"Now you *are* being stupid. They are nice people with good manners at the Timberlodge Club."

That hurt. Mary's parents could readily afford the cost of membership, kitting out their daughter immaculately, a brand new racquet – in order to play at the exclusive club, where everyone ran and leapt about clad, not just in white togs, but spotlessly white tennis clothes. Jim thought glumly that if he ever played tennis, it would be in old grey flannels, dingy grey plimsolls, a white shirt (sleeves rolled up) – and with a racquet borrowed from a cousin.

"That's as may be. But I don't think it's good manners to turn up half an hour late for our date. And not for the first time either."

Mary bit her lower lip with vexation.

"I don't care, it's not up to you Jim to tell me what to do. You're not going to run my life."

"I don't want to; but this isn't good enough leaving me hanging about. You're just taking me for granted."

"Don't be silly. You're just jealous because I've got other friends. And anyway, it's you who take me for granted."

"How do you make that out?"

"Well, what about all that mud and rain you trailed me through at Elmdon?"

"So I'm to blame for the weather now, am I?"

"Oh, don't be so stupid."

"I'm not, that is why I don't come running at your beck and call," a phrase he had picked up from his mother.

"Boys are stupid."

"And I suppose girls are regular little Einsteins."

"Oh shut up! There's no sense in talking to you when you're like this."

Jim knew it was a mistake but anger, resentment and hurt feelings having got the better of reason, he launched into bitter sarcasms. Came a lull in the sharp volley and return exchanges;

"See you tomorrow. I hope you won't be late."

Mary flushed angrily but made no reply and walked towards her home, viciously swishing her racquet, but still looking so young, so pretty in her spotless tennis dress.

That evening, Jim confided to his diary; "made some sarcastic remarks which I know I will be sorry for later."

For once, Jim was right. On Black Friday:

"Had my cards (the sack) from Mary in a note brought by Dickie. Doesn't want to see me again. Can't come out tonight. Doesn't like going out with boys." Sarcastic snort from the reader. "Can still be friends (?)" How like a girl – wanting to have a cake and eat it.

Still, on a second and cooler reading, or maybe it was the third or fourth, Jim recognised that not all bridges had been burned. He applied his developing analytical skills to this heart-rending English composition: 'Doesn't want to see me again;' 'Can't come out tonight,' surely there was encouraging ambiguity there? Again, 'doesn't like going out with boys' hardly tied in neatly with 'can still be friends', with or without the question mark. Given the trouble Mary had with some of her spellings, and various grammatical points, she would hardly want to remain just a penfriend?

So Jim picked up his few crumbs of consolation but resolutely resolved that he'd be damned if he'd write a letter of apology. He acknowledged that he had spoken harshly to the girl who was his girl no more, and he was sincerely sorry for that as he had told his diary. But, damn it, he had been sorely provoked and he remained convinced that Mary had begun to give him the run around, to take him for granted. No, he wasn't going to share his brother-in-law's fate. Bill could please himself, or rather he couldn't please himself, but was contentedly conditioned to his hen-pecked role. No, Jim inwardly reaffirmed that he, personally, was made of more mettlesome stuff.

So Jim continued to brood about women and their peculiar, tiresome and tiresomely peculiar ways. His rudeness and boorish behaviour apart, on that evening of volley and smash, did Mary have other reasons for giving him the old 'heave-ho'? Having attained some unrevealed goal of her own, relating to his enamoured state and reactions, had she decided that he could now be safely set to one side, to cool his heels and so on, while she experimented with other friendships? She might well reason to herself that 'reliable old Jim', enthralled as he was, could be recalled to her side, if and when appropriate, by a note, a date to meet, the skilful use of those large, bewitching eyes?

If that was the way of it, then she had another think coming. But damnation, he was still in love with her!

His thoughts moved on to marriages within his own family. As far as he could recall, the young ladies, before they became his sisters-in-law, had all seemed so pleasant, so anxious to please, so ready to defer to the ideas, whims and wishes of their husbands-to-be. And then, at varying periods after they had become wives – wham, bam! It was as though a steel trap had been sprung – snap! Gotcha! Sweetness and honey replaced by tartness and vinegar. Turn a freedom loving terrier into a stay at home poodle. That seemed to be their game. Small wonder there were so few songs about the joys of wedlock.

Again Jim thought of Bill. As he did so, another of his Dad's music hall songs came to mind.

"I'm Billy Juggins,
Commonly known as a muggins.
Silly, Billy,
That's what my friends call me..."

If Bill was willing to be a slave – OK – that was up to him. Bill's own disposition moved him that way. But it was no way for a Jim Norton to go, no siree. And yet, once a girl, after all, she was a woman in the making, had got her emotional hooks into you, even a Houdini wouldn't be able to wriggle free. Growing up was a jolly sight more difficult than many grown ups would have you believe. It was high time, thought Jim, that he consulted his friendly analyst.

Stretched out on 'the beast', that black horsehair sofa at his Gran's (long trousers afforded better protection now) Jim spoke feelingly, but self-mockingly, of 'the iron having been burned deeper in his soul' – the Bertie Wooster influence at work. Jim's mom listened patiently, sympathetically, but gave little advice: "I should leave things as they are for the time being son. There are plenty of more fish in the sea you know."

This was not the kind of advice Jim wanted to hear. He had no desire at all to resume fishing trips with Ken. Why, oh why, oh why, couldn't bluebells bloom for ever?

Having been given his marching orders by Mary, (an action he still couldn't fully "comprehend") Jim was free to join the twelve mile ramble through leafy Warwickshire, organised by Mr Martin for that boisterous Sunday School class of Dave, Bob et al, that was to dissolve on the morrow. The cheerful, bantering company, the scenery and the "A1 tea at a farmhouse" all helped to take Jim's mind "off more unpleasant thoughts." He even began to feel for others again. "Harry Martin must be lots of money out of pocket, even though we gave him 1/6 each." A decent old stick Harry.

My, but it was good to be in manly company again.

He recalled one of his Dad's favourite quotations from Byron's *Don Juan*,

"Man's love is of man's life a thing apart,
'Tis woman's whole existence."
Spot on that, milord.

More of the manly, healthy outdoor life shortly followed, when
Jim became one of an advance party to set up the school camp in
Abergele. Of course, there were some drawbacks to the great
outdoors – an over plentiful supply of Welsh rain – and two totally
obnoxious, stinking in fact, fags among the lads in Jim's tent. But
there was a Spartan heroic side to the 'holiday' as well – a hazardous
scramble up, and a skin grazing slide part way down a mountain,
bathing in the chilly sea, and being stung by a wasp. Rollicking fun
though in Rhyl, on the pleasure beach, where the wastrel blued in
"about six shillings" – and then a raucous sing-song around "a big
camp fire..."

"Who's got eyes as black as night,
Wheezy Anna,
One looks left and the other looks right,
Wheezy Anna.

Wheezy Anna, Wheezy Anna
Down where the water melons grow.
And they've all got pips in,
Wheezy Anna, Wheezy Anna,
She is the sweetest girl I know."

'Well not quite – or rather, not by a long chalk,' thought Jim.

Next morning, seated on the back of the lorry, packed with poles,
sodden canvas and ground-sheets, Jim waited for the driver to set off
for Brum.

"Hey, hang on a minute. Here's a letter for you Norton. It looks
like a girl's handwriting."

The master winked. Jim almost winked back. Certainly it was
writing that Jim recognised. His heart leapt. Mary had written to say
she was going on holiday. Nothing unusual or special about that,
lucky thing – but "she says 'au revoir' Hopeful!" Indeed it was, but
Jim spent a lot of time next day wondering "what to write and say to
Mary without making myself 'cheap' in any way." Friendly but firm,
that's what he'd be. He'd be no dame's pushover. Cue for a song
Al, pal.

"I suppose I should forget you,
If I had an ounce of pride,
But I guess I can't help being
On the sentimental side..."

The summer hols, for some, were now in full swing. Doug, Bob, Dave, Ken, Syd Whitley – had all gone away. Dandy Sandy, would-be expert at ping-pong and ballroom dancing, had started work. Jim wondered how Dandy would like office life, in the august Council House, solemnity in every imposing Municipal stone. Likeable and amusing lad though he was, he surely wouldn't be able to vent his bubbly spirits in the manner of a true sixth former. Would he really dare to plant a whoopee cushion on a pompous chairman's seat? Jim looked back to a June entry in his diary and smiled at the recollection;

"Dandy fooled around in Private Study as usual, so Doug and I beat him up in the form room afterwards. Took his shoes and socks off, and sock suspenders. Tied the latter round his forehead. He got quite wild. Slung chairs about, and emptied waste paper box. He upset our desks and books, after we had gone. We went back and tidied up. He'll be all right tomorrow."

Good old Dandy – sure to be a tonic for local government.

Jim wondered what it must be like, working for money.

A cheerful voice broke through his reverie.

"Guy Squint, our kid, them's great gladdies you've got there. You're a cert to win again."

Harold smiled, a little complacently, pleased at his brother's genuine compliment. He made a final, unnecessary adjustment to the bunch of ramrod stiff, immaculate sword lilies in his massive fist. No one knew who Guy Squint was, not even Les, but the expression always prefaced a compliment or remark of surprise made by Les.

"Guy Squint Junior, stop moping. Birds can be very temperamental you know, especially at certain times – and I'm talking from experience. Do snap out of it. Tell you what – you can borrow my bike, if you like, while I'm away on holiday. But just mind you don't muck it up."

Les was 'hot stuff' on keeping his clothes, his overalls, work and garden tools, his own appearance – and that of his push-bike – in scrupulously clean, neat, and good working order.

So, gratefully pedalling away, Jim began to explore some of the small towns lying to the north of Birmingham – Coleshill, Aldridge, Tamworth and Lichfield. He was deeply impressed by Lichfield's cathedral – but not in any spiritual manner. Rather, as a former wood whittler himself, did he marvel at the exquisitely beautiful craftsmanship so richly and intricately in evidence. He wondered what such skilled, gifted and dedicated workmen had earned by way of earthly reward.

Whatever his present status, Jim remembered that as a boy, he had whittled, with his penknife, from a triangular sectioned piece of firewood, a figure that had looked for all the world like an Easter Island statue. He had set a couple of his Dad's paste 'gems', a bright blue, into the head, as eyes. A centrally placed 'ruby' had ennobled the lofty forehead. And, as a crowning glory, and good luck totem, he had fixed, with plastic wood, above the ruby, one of his own double milk teeth. He sighed, life had seemed so much simpler in those far gone days.

Soon he was back in Lichfield once more, this time with Ken, newly returned from Derbyshire. Ken looked a bit different but behaved as before.

"He started his old game when he got there...seems absolutely impossible for him to keep away from girls," whether near the cathedral or in Perry Park where Territorial Army soldiers were in camp, providing stiff competition for Ken, even when decked out in his smart new finery.

Ken now sported a fashionable pork pie hat and an old boys' tie, for he had landed an office job at the GEC, Witton. Doubtless, he sensed the favourable contrast he would make, as a white collar sophisticate, to his schoolboy gawk of a friend. After all, Ken would only be interested in his chosen girl of a pair. Further rebellion was not on the cards since Mary had 'disappeared', and Jim (maybe temporarily, maybe not), seemed totally disinterested in other wenches.

Gawk or not, Jim wasn't really sure whether he was still a schoolboy. He had not been entered for the Subsidiary exams taken a year before Higher School Certificate. True, he had sat comparable tests because the teachers concerned were keen that he should stay on for another year and 'have a go' for the HSC. His Dad had not yet made formal application for him to leave school, and so Jim remained nominally on the school roll, troubled in mind, anxious about the future and not just because it "LOOKS LIKE WAR AGAIN" (21st August).

He now knew his mom to be fighting a valiant rearguard action, on his behalf, to keep him at school. Knowing her son, and what he had achieved, Sal was confident that, given the chance, Jim would gain his HSC. She herself had always wanted to be a teacher, a desire frustrated by poverty.

Wilf stuck stubbornly to his Victorian guns. His own schooling had finished near enough a quarter of a century before the outbreak of World War I. And while he didn't expect Jim to start work, like himself, as an errand-boy – he did expect him to start work. In his view, Jim had already received a good education and could, no doubt, get a decent job now. His pals – Ken, for instance, and that Dandy Sandy he talked about – were in work. Dave soon would be. Money was always tight and one regular pay-packet in the home, junior size though it might be, would be a godsend.

The struggle between Sal and Wilf over Jim's future continued – and the wider world itself edged closer to self-destruction.

Announcement of the mutual non-aggression pact between alleged arch enemies Germany and the Soviet Union, proved a real 'shaker' for Britain and France, for it left the way clear for Germany to invade Poland without opposition. Jim made a confident prediction;

"I believe the Russo-German Pact has ulterior motive in communising Europe after a war when people will be so impoverished they will rise against their rulers."

Jim not only helped with prediction but with pickaxe as well, helping others to dig large holes in back-gardens – first at Doug's in Great Barr – and then at Dave's in Perry Barr, holes adequate to house the Anderson ARP shelters – 6' 6" X 4' 6", was it? The pace of preparation quickened – blackout material for windows was bought. Phil was called up, then Alec, to Gosport. Both these half brothers were RAF reservists, and had served as volunteers on mine-sweepers at the end of World War I.

From South Devon, from Paignton – came better news, from Mary – staying at a holiday camp.

"Very friendly letter. Tons of mistakes as per usual. Gladdened my heart." (Not the English mistakes but the tone of the letter). Jim replied next day and then went to watch the Villa beat Middlesborough

2 – 0. Verdict: "Very good game. Nobody suffering from crisitis. First thing the men did at the match when they bought evening papers was to look at racing results on the back page. Typical illustration of man-in-street's unconcern."

But then, out of a clear sky, "Disastrous news! Got to go to school tomorrow." On the morrow, "I think the idea is to take the kids' minds off the situation." On 1st September, the day when partridge shooting officially began, Jim felt a shade lugubrious, for evacuation meant saying "goodbye to all my pals. May never see them again... went to the Birchfields to try and forget the catastrophe which looms over us."

The film – with Boris Karloff now transmuted from Frankenstein to a Chinese sleuth, Mr Wong (leave the puns alone) – was not a deal of help.

*

On 2nd September Jim, aged sixteen and five months declared, quite succinctly, his initial war aims;

"I hope to join Navy when I'm seventeen. Shall have a job to persuade Mom and Dad since Phil will be in France when war is declared and Alec is at Gosport and Ted will probably have to go and John was killed twenty-one years ago on Thursday. Still I don't want to stay at home doing nothing unless I can go to school, get my Higher Certif, play for 1sts and win the cup again."

Chapter Ten
Limbo and Luck

"What do you think will happen now?"

For a moment, the question hung in the air as Bob and Jim both glanced involuntarily towards the sky. They were sauntering on a lovely warm, sunny day, across Perry Playing Fields. A sombre morning church service was over on 'the day war broke out.'

"It's difficult to say," replied Bob, a tall, fair-haired lad, a year or so older than his friend, and fellow ex-member of the 'plague Mr Martin' squad. Bob might already have pictured himself in smart RAF uniform, but could have had no conception of years of service in the North African desert under the searing, unrelenting, skin cancer inducing sun.

"I suppose the Maginot and Siegfried Lines could start bashing one another," he continued, "and I suppose there could be some skirmishing in no-man's land."

"Yes, I suppose that's right. Anyway, I hope Winston Churchill will join the cabinet."

"Me too – it needs some backbone."

Jim looked skywards again.

"When do you think we'll get our first air raid?"

"Not before we've got our air raid shelter, I hope!"

"Amen to that!"

The lads chuckled.

"Anyway, whether the bombs drop sooner or later, I've got a job which I'll probably keep 'til I join up. But what about your own future Jim? Will the school at Grove Lane reopen – and will you go back?"

"I jolly well wish I knew. I'd rather go to Stroud really cos that's where most of the sixth form have gone. But I don't even know whether I'm staying on. I think Dad will have to go to the Education Office in Margaret Street up town, to sort things out."

The friends continued walking towards the river and the back of the greyhound racing track.

"Talking of Spitfires, which we weren't – and no offence intended, how's your Mary by the way?"

Yes, that's how she was still spoken of, as 'Jim's Mary'. Perhaps that had been part of the problem, their problem – Jim's possessiveness? Jim remained unsure. Had he ever been talked of in feminine circles as – 'Mary's Jim?' Quite possibly he thought – ladies were no slouches at claiming 'rights' – at getting their danders up – if they thought poachers were on the prowl. Enough of introspection he thought. There was a war on – which might go on and on, and tragedy had already struck brutally at too many lives.

On the second day of the war news came, as Jim recorded in what was now 'a war journal', that the "British unarmed liner *Athenia* torpedoed and sunk by a submarine undoubtedly German." (one hundred and twelve lives lost).

A few days later contrasting cheering news arrived from Stroud. Doug had been digging trenches – so had Syd Whitley. It was heart warmingly reassuring to find that facetious schoolboy humour had not become an early wartime casualty.

After all the earlier bumbling and fumbling concerning Munich – the appeasement vs. rearmament debate, it was good to know that in a free country, post, bus, rail and housing services could still operate efficiently – *vide* Syd's letter.

"Dear Alf, (Jim was Alf to Lionel's Syd)

We left school...in buses, and the train left New Street on the dot and arrived in like manner. You can tell how marvellously the arrangements were made. The billets are very comfortable... Stroud itself is a very nice town but there are hills, hills, hills and then some hills...Tomorrow we sally forth to dig trenches, national defence and all that you know, so think of me wielding a deft pick and deftly picking my way to Australia... the only snag so far is that we all have to be in our billets by 7.30 but successful evasions of masters have been carried out by..."

There followed a description of the various crafty dodges employed.

Jim's heart ached to make his muscles ache like those of the merry pick swingers, probably bellowing – 'Hi ho, hi ho, it's off to dig we go' – during pauses between swings. Jim could just imagine it. Great fun. Lucky devils.

He dispiritedly picked up a *Short History of French Literature* in what now seemed the increasingly forlorn hope that he would return to school, either in Birmingham or Stroud.

"Beaumarchais' dramatic work is of a piece with his life, and his great creation, the character of Figaro, we might almost call a dramatisation of himself. The valet, capable, scheming, restlessly active, feeling his own ability and embittered by the want of recognition which he receives at the hands of society, is Beaumarchais himself..."

Jim felt he could sympathise. Trouble was, he Jim, was not only "restlessly active" but restlessly inactive into the bargain. He had entered a dreary, fallow period of his life, no school, no job, no girl – and, what was worse in a way, no inclination, yet, to seek another girl.

To cope with the "restlessly active" Jim took himself off for long solitary walks – and long spells of rowing on park pools – his yearning thoughts so often with Mary.

News from the war fronts was depressing too. The Poles, although fighting valiantly, were clearly losing the battle for Warsaw. *HMS Courageous*, an aircraft carrier "was torpedoed and sunk by U Boat", with the loss of five hundred British sailors. (Alec, fortunately, was serving on the carrier the *Ark Royal*). A few weeks later another savage setback – the sinking of the *Royal Oak* – 800 plus dead – and a sickening blow to national morale, for this mighty battleship had been torpedoed in its 'impregnable' home base of Scapa Flow.

Although tactical issues concerning – *** (kisses remember) had taken a back seat, Jim's diary showed no loss of interest in global strategy.

With Russia now having invaded Poland from the east; "War practically over in Poland. Warsaw still holding out. Many ways of looking at present situation. Stalin might be leading Hitler up garden path. Hope so. On the other hand Hitler when he is losing might throw his lot in with us to prop up Capitalism and destroy Communism which is bound to follow in most countries after conclusion of war. Rumours flying around. Goebbels missing etc."

Then, quite suddenly, news from the heartthrob front to set the spirits a dancing, a "very friendly letter" from Mary. "Hooray! Lots of cheers." It was a relief to know, that Mary was now 'safely' housed at Worcester, with relatives.

And, on the home front, "Things aren't too bad." No air raids, no gas attacks. Within a few weeks of their enforced closure, cinemas reopened, the Government recognising the importance to morale of the escapism conjured up by Hollywood, especially with winter approaching. Long blackout hours seemed likely to be dreary, dismal, demoralising. Phew! Straightway, Jim went to shiver at *The Son of Frankenstein*: "100% better than its predecessor. Thrilling."

Eventually, an air raid shelter arrived for 'the dump', and neighbouring homes. But Wilf wouldn't accept delivery! Jim was present at the time.

"Did Dad carry on! I'll say. The air was blue for miles around."

While it wasn't compulsory to take an Anderson shelter, Jim didn't dare ask why his Dad was so madly stick waving furious, against sheltering from possible bombs. It wasn't as though the garden was much cop as a tiny part of the now threatened 'green and pleasant land'. The soil seemed an impoverished mixture of what might be thin, unhealthy earth, certainly fine ash and most decidedly 'cat mess'.

For possible guidance about his Dad's incandescent anger, Jim turned to his Wills' set of 'Air Raid Precautions'. No, nothing there about the psychological aspects of sheltering from air raids. Plenty of sound practical advice though, distributed among the 50 cards. Jim paused at card No. 3, 'Making A Door Gas-Proof' – by fastening a suitably sized carpet or blanket over the door. There'd be few, if any blankets to spare in his home and certainly no bits of carpet, large or thick enough, to fit the bill. He chuckled as he conjured up an image of a motley assemblage of badly worn hearth and bedside rugs nailed across a door. He was sure Pop wouldn't wear that precaution either.

Returning to the cards, he was interested to see that a small group of them described 'how to tackle an incendiary bomb', the competent tackling being demonstrated by a smartly dressed, matronly looking lady, a middle class housewife presumably, her husband away in the forces or on war work. Would Jim's mom be able to cope? Naturally, she would first insist on putting on her pinny. Yes, Jim thought she'd measure up OK. While it was dangerous, tackling an incendiary bomb did not seem like heavy work. And he'd be there to help or take over – until he joined up. Another few months and he'd be seventeen – and then the Navy? And then?

He was slipping into that Hamlet mood again – Hamlet, the kind of chap who would be sitting among smouldering, stench-laden ruins, before he reached for a bucket of sand.

Jim promptly went into next door's garden and set about helping to dig out the hole for the sensible Ridgeways' shelter.

Though nominally free, the corrugated metal sheets (that Mr Ridgeway and Jim struggled with), and much else besides, still had to be paid for. In late September an Emergency Budget was introduced;

"Sugar up 1d lb. Beer 1d pt. Income tax raised to 7s 6d." (37.5 % in the pound – a record).

*

Slowly, cautiously, people began to restore, as much as they could, the reassuring patterns of peacetime to their newly disrupted lives. Jim walked to The Hawthorns, quite a step, a good couple of miles, to watch a keen derby match – "Baggies" vs. "Wolves.": "Westcott a real live wire leader for the Wolves. Banged in 3 peach goals for them." What higher praise could there be?

Thanks to the initiative of Ron, one of the Jackson twins, a new football team, of high promise, was formed from old 5C and sixth formers – including Jack Lloyd, Thomas and Dandy. The 'Bridge FC', black knicks, white shirts – fixtures, home and away at Perry Playing Fields. The spirit of the future nation was still alive, and shortly to be vigorously kicking.

Guild meetings started up again – Jim accompanied the new wage slaves, Dave and Ken, but not for long, as the claims of evening classes (theirs not Jim's) merited higher priority.

Time dribbled away; air raids started, mostly on naval bases. "150,000 British troops have been moved to France in five weeks..." Prime minister Chamberlain had made a fine speech. "I expect he feels that Churchill will soon kick him out." Men aged twenty to twenty-two were to be conscripted.

Jim, the regular picture-goer re-enlisted, going with Bob to see *The Four Feathers*, the heroic side of war; and on his own to enjoy *Idiot's Delight*, a fine anti-war film starring Norma Shearer and Clark Gable.

Although he didn't find the words right away, Jim sensed rather than clearly thought, what a strong, tolerant democracy Britain must basically be, to allow the screening of such a film at such a time. But the film's 'futility of war' message was not stridently presented, and 'sugar' sweetened the 'pill', Clark Gable 'hoofin' it', and impressively at that, flanked either side by three pretty chorus girls, all tap-dancing to 'Putting on the Ritz' as the world set about destroying itself.

*

"What do you think of him then Pop?"

"Who?"

"This chap."

Jim held up a copy of *Illustrated*, pointing to the front cover fully occupied by an enlarged face of "Bulldog Churchill", a slight smile on his lips but looking grimly determined.

"Oh him. Well, he's no friend of the working class and he made a hash of things at Gallipoli. But he'd certainly make a better fist of things than Chamberlain."

Jim turned the pages of the magazine which had dropped *Weekly* from its title.

A two page spread, mostly of photographs and maps entitled "Outflanking the Maginot Line" prompted some uneasy thoughts. Were there weak spots in the frontiers of Holland, Belgium, Switzerland? The defences shown seemed puny when compared to the massive underground fortifications of the French Maginot Line.

Jim retreated to "Blackout Blues" merry making scenes from London night life. "Who'd mind an air raid in a shelter full of glamour girls?" 'A purely, or perhaps impurely rhetorical question as far as he was concerned,' thought Jim. London, and real live glamour were a universe distant. He looked to the left of the caption. What a stunner!

A wide-eyed blonde, with a mass of curly hair, high heeled shoes – and very little in between. Well, a skimpy bra, and what looked like a piece of string. A delightful figure, without a doubt – and yet, in an odd way, the picture seemed obscene. Eyes apart, this lissom, showgirl's features were grotesquely concealed behind – a gas mask. A new and hideous twist to beauty and the beast.

*

Suddenly, events moved swiftly. Birmingham's Education Committee ruled that if one Jim Norton was to leave school, then the £13 and a few bob already paid towards his education for 1939/40 would have to be repaid. 'Whoopee!' Jim rejoiced. He knew that by now, late October, nowhere near such a sum in ready cash would be available in the bread and scrape Norton household. A fig for the whys and wherefores of the shortfall. Pack the suitcase and head for the Cotswold Hills.

First find your suitcase. Jim had to push aside his dad's easy chair, in order to open the door to the narrow, crooked-leg stairway.

On entering the tiny, neglected back bedroom, Jim wrinkled his nose with disgust – not at the slight but pervasive smell of chilly damp, but at the general run down appearance of this hutch of a boxroom. In a few places, crumbling, faded pink plaster had fallen in to expose bare, grey, warped laths. A low, whitewashed ceiling, flakily pock marked, loured above.

Almost the length of one wall, squatted the crudely built and monstrous base, of what had been a cumbersome wooden bookcase, in an alcove of the dining room at 'the old house.' Against the opposite wall stood, in tipsy fashion – one castor short, a 'marble' topped washstand, a corner chipped off the marble, the mirror cracked. A chamber pot, both chipped and cracked stood on the shelf below together with a water jug, a chip at its spout. The cheap lino – only partly covering the floor, was cracked near to the point of being crazed. Crikey, wouldn't he be glad to get away, maybe out of the frying pan into the fire, but he might be lucky and land a good billet.

Having found the suitcase, Jim stopped to look at the one object of real value in the room – a battered, splintering tea chest. Just an old, commonplace tea chest – from the outside – but an Aladdin's cave within, to those who possessed the magic password to boyhood memories – and Jim most certainly did.

Underneath a bit of old curtain, (to keep off the dust and scurfy whitewash) lay precious reminders of his happy days at 'the old home'. Jim knew well enough that a strong sentimental streak resided in his make-up – just as it did in his dad's. Had his mom had her way, she would have thrown 'all that perishin' junk' into the dustbin ages ago. He reflected that the so-called gentler sex, could, on occasion, be astonishingly insensitive. Downright unimaginative sometimes.

Yes, he'd have one more look before becoming an evacuee. Who knew? Would such treasures still be there whenever he next came home? Would there be a home to come home to?

Jim checked his maudlin line of thought by removing the dust cover, picking up and examining each treasure with loving care. The grey painted fort that Bill had so readily made for him. He vividly remembered his brother-in-law spreading glue across the square and then sprinkling fine hard sand over the drying, tacky surface. The result – a real, rasping parade ground sound when Jim's soldier lads marched smartly across. A few of that gallant, intrepid band remained, mostly Scotties – a handful only with a full complement of limbs.

Next to hand appeared some 'Topical Times' footballers. He had glued these photographs with Secotine on to cardboard, adding a bent section of card at the back to serve as a support. In this way, 'Pongo' Waring, Eric Houghton, Cliff Bastin and other sturdy heroes had stood on his chest of drawers at 96.

A shoebox held a pile of 1d albums for sticky backs: 'British Fresh-Water Fishes'; 'Hints on Association Football'; 'Radio Celebrities' – and the like. All complete and reasonably clean.

In a small Oxo tin – a maritime museum. The last resting place of the Armada, and British sea dogs' vessels. Galleons had been fashioned, by a dextrous whittle, from acorns, (now sadly shrivelled), paper sails pierced by pins for masts. In their cigarette packet pits, snarled the wonderful racing beasts of Birkin, Eyston, Cobb and Howe – soon to be duelling round the steeply banked track of Brooklands. Jim carefully examined each lovingly whittled piece of wood, wheels of white linen shirt buttons, the rims painted black. He straightened one or two axles (good job his mom was something of a needlewoman) and put the Bentley and its rivals carefully on the washstand.

The prize, perhaps, of the collection was the 'Golden Arrow'; a tin plate toy quite 18" long, its gold paint scratched, its tail fin buckled and bent and the on-side front wheel missing. Did the clockwork motor still work? Jim tried it – yes, it did – but he made a mental note to give it a spot of oil before he left for Stroud.

Such a vivid reminder, the turning of that key, of the time when as a small boy, he had stood gazing open mouthed and pop-eyed at the 'real live' Golden Arrow, placed on display in Birmingham's Bingley Hall. "On 11th March, 1929, this wonderful car covered a flying mile at a mean speed of 231.36 miles an hour, thereby beating the world's land speed record." So a cigarette card informed the reader.

Jim rummaged further and fished to the surface a small bundle of comics and boys' magazines. To think he had once enjoyed the babyish *Tiny Tots* and *Tiger Tim's Weekly*! He passed quickly to the penny comics – *Comic Cuts*, *Funny Wonder*, with its strip cartoon adventures of Charlie Chaplin, King of the Kinema – and *Chips*, with "The Merry Adventures of Weary Willie and Tired Tim." He turned to page two:

"Cross Talk
Jolly Jests by Wilfred and Walter.
"…tell me which is the smallest bridge in the world?"
"The bridge of your nose, of course! Any donkey knows that!"
"So I noticed!""

He picked up *Comic Cuts*.
"Teacher: "In walking along a fence a cat always uses its tail to balance itself."
Smart Sammy: "Please sir, what does a Manx cat do, then?""

Jim smirked – not a bad question – for 1925.

*

A plaintive cry reached Jim's ears.
"What on earth   are you doing James?   There's a thunderin' draught down here with the doors open. Do hurry up!"
"Shan't be long now."

His mom could at least shut the door to the staircase. 'Why didn't she?' he wondered. Probably counting stitches again, for the new pullover she was knitting for him to take to Stroud. When she gave it to him, she would doubtless crack the old chestnut – 'Winter draw(er)s on you know.' He smiled.

"Well, look sharp about it. Sharp's the word and Sharps the toffee, you know."

Jim turned to glance at *Adventure*, *The Hotspur* and then *The Magnet*. Come to think of it, these precious archives were indicative of his intellectual growth – at least on the lighter side. What might follow? What indeed? He'd keep an open mind.

"James, I shan't tell you again."

"Only a minute now Ma."

"And don't call me Ma!"

Jim made a last dive into the tea chest.

Hallelujah! Still intact – his good luck totem, the Easter Island whittle, now with only one eye, but the tooth still firmly in place.

He carefully replaced these artefacts from a past civilisation and clumped downstairs, quite forgetting to take the suitcase.

The next few days could well be characterised as happy daze.

The Head wrote to say he was "very pleased I am going...Hooray, three cheers etc."...and, "Uncle Les shook hands with King" (during a royal visit to Kynochs – Witton, major ammunition producers). Life all round had bucked up enormously. Even the Bridge FC's defeat by the one goal scored, was excusable – same old trouble "our attack was very weak."

Sticking still to his own maxim of 'fair play's a jewel,' Jim's dad remained a gracious loser in the struggle over educational policy. Early on Sunday morning, this family of three trudged across Handsworth Park to the coach garage, more than a mile away.

A curious threesome in some ways – a father aged sixty-one, who already had nine grandchildren, swinging forward his stiff right leg in rhythm with his rubber ferruled stick – a middle aged woman of doughty spirit but physically rather frail, always a few paces ahead of her husband – and a mixture of boy, lad and youth of sixteen moving back and forth between his parents. But the three, looking rather like refugees in the making, cared for one another in their different ways, and in a cheerfully grumbling manner swapped around the "two heavy suitcases" for carrying. At last, Jim was on his way to a totally new and invigorating environment.

*

"Wotcher Alf."

"Wotcher Syd."

Broad grins from both lads.

"Mr and Mrs Appleton, this is Jim Norton."

The elderly couple smiled reassuringly at their new charge.

"Jim, I call him Alf, is a bit of a card sharp but he has his good points."

"Well, another crib player would come in handy. Do you happen to play crib lad?"

Mr Appleton's light blue eyes twinkled.

As befitting a seasoned crib player, Jim made a guarded response: too early to show much of his hand yet. Some measure had first to be taken of the competition.

"I have played a few times, mostly with one of my uncles, who has given me a few tips. But pegging out well is still something of a mystery."

(That last claim was rank deceit, but consistent with Jim's intention to play his cards cautiously.)

"Well, so long as you don't peg out while you're with us, things will be all right."

Pa Appleton chuckled at his own 'witticism'.

"But you'll find Ma's cooking is just fine."

"Pay no attention to Pa's little jokes. We'll try and make you comfortable. I know Syd, as you call him, has never left anything on his plate."

Syd grinned broadly and nodded his agreement.

Jim soon felt thoroughly at home with this "very nice couple." Ma Appleton seemed like an older version of his mom – not so round faced but with a similar gentle smile, and very similar flowered pinafore. Pa resembled a younger version of his grandad – the moustache more walrus-like certainly, but then Pa Appleton had served as a merchant seaman in the days of sail.

These new 'parents' worked as caretakers in a primary school in the town centre, and lived in a house adjoining the school. On that very first evening, out came a deck of cards and the crib board. Watch out Uncle Les, Jim had embarked on an intensive course of 'pegging out' improvement.

Next day, another good start for the born again schoolboy.

"Had quite a welcome. Grand to see old faces. Doug absolutely delighted and even the masters gave me a welcome."

Naturally, the Marling School for Boys wasn't a patch on HGS with its super new gym. Still, the school's fine stone exterior looked fresh and clean, not smoke and soot begrimed. And its level, well-grassed playing fields were literally on the school doorstep. Yippee!

Jim soon learned that 'schooling' meant half-time schooling, Marling sharing its premises on a time basis with the Brummagem interlopers – the separate groups of boys boxing and coxing, one week mornings, one week afternoons.

On the first morning, Jim acknowledged that he would "have a lot of work to catch up." So, to clear his head for impending intellectual trials he "climbed up Rodborough Hill this aft. with Doug. Beautiful day and marvellous view...beautiful countryside."

After natural beauty, mean and ugly human behaviour, for next day, after playing football, he found that "someone had half-inched my purse which contained over 9s for books." Immediately he had to write home for help and received two 2/- postal orders by return. The Headmaster sportingly offered to lend him money, but Jim refused. He preferred independence and remaining "short of cash for a bit" – to debt. In fact, he rather agreed with Polonius;

"Neither a borrower, nor a lender be."

But as a student, and therefore critic of *Hamlet*, Jim held to the view, that the old codger who had been stabbed through the arras, had been laying down the law only in relation to money, jewels, gold and similar loot. He had said nothing about bicycles.

While Jim was never entirely comfortable when asking a fellow schoolboy for the loan of a bike, the desire to explore 'his' corner of the Cotswolds overcame his unrevealed discomfiture at placing himself under an obligation, and signalling that he and his parents were less well off than many others.

But once the pedals were turning, cares were forgotten, as in the company of Syd, Doug, sometimes 'Chub', he visited Painswick, Minchinhampton, Cranham, Bisley, Birdlip, Gloucester cathedral, Tewkesbury Abbey, Cirencester – and that favourite – Slad Valley with its "marvellous autumnal tints".

By the end of the first week in Stroud, he had tracked down that ex-Don R (dispatch rider) Dickie. He learned that Mary had moved to a new address in Worcester, which Dickie himself was visiting that weekend.

"Told Dickie to give her my kind regards."

Perhaps a touch austere that, so the following day Jim wrote a letter – and hoped. So did others, with quite different and totally unromantic objectives.

8th November, 1939 entered the history books as the day when an attempt to kill Hitler, with a time-bomb in a Munich Bierkeller failed. Knowing nothing of this on the day, Jim recorded immense relief at an 'escape' from potential 'disaster'. "Medically examined and I was overjoyed to hear that there was nothing wrong with my feet, so I can run & run & run."

Some twerp had made a chance remark about the low state of Jim's arches – and for a period he had experienced torturing anxieties that he might be developing flat feet, and so be prevented from joining up and from running, if not like a greyhound, then at least like a nimble fox terrier.

Based on British newspaper reports, Jim dismissed, with withering schoolboy scorn, the official German accounts of who was responsible for the 'outrage' in the bierkeller.

"Jews, British secret service and Government. Must have mentality of child. Some say it was planned to show German people that providence was looking after the mighty Hitler. I should laugh. Freedom Station said at night that it was only the first of many attempts. That's the stuff."

Hitler had been lucky. Having delivered a typical rant and trumpeted that Germany was prepared for a five year war against Britain, he had unexpectedly been called away, half an hour too early to benefit mankind. A 'what if' situation, if ever there was one, to exercise deeply the imagination.

So then, deeply disappointing news on 9th November when gloomy blackout hours ran from 16.50 to 07.40. But next day, all was light and bright and cheerful again for "the long awaited epistle" arrived. "No, I haven't forgotten you," wrote Mary, "just darn opposite." Jim read and re-read that magical phrase – "Just darn opposite." Not only "Yippee!" but, "Hooray, hooray, hooray".

A fortnight later, came additional heartening news. Mary "might be coming to Stroud soon. Wants to know if I will see her. Will I? I should say so. Learnt yesterday that we break up on 22nd. Ten days leave but parents must accept full responsibility for boys safety. Still I shall go home. Hope to see Mary then."

Jim smiled, a little sardonically. Here was evidence of 'bridge building' that needed no bellowing by six hundred grammar school

boys – nothing so vaultingly ambitious as joining nation unto nation—
more a tender, gentle movement from girl to boy and boy to girl.
   "Hands across the table
   When the lights are low..."

Chapter Eleven
Home Front – Away and Home

"Here – catch!"

"You silly ass!"

Syd made a desperate lunge to grip the orange, carelessly lobbed to him by Alf, from the opposite side of their bedroom.

A tall gangling lad, a little clumsy in his movements and slightly splay footed, Syd was no natural ball player and certainly no lightning reaction slip fielder.

"Look out!"

Alf's warning cry proved to be in vain. A flailing elbow had struck a blue china vase standing on the narrow mantelpiece. The vase slowly toppled and Syd made a wild grab to save it.

"Good as a comic strip to see Syd frantically clutching at a vase which was slipping from his fingers to its doom on the fender beneath. Such is life."

Well, not quite. It was not pleasant to be reminded by one's second mother, that lads of sixteen should not behave like young roughnecks of thirteen. Syd and Alf felt duly ashamed. "Still it was funny though", not the gentle more in sorrow than in anger, ticking off, which they had undoubtedly 'urned' ho! ho! – but Syd's unacrobatic attempts to be acrobatic.

"Atmosphere a little strained at breakfast but cleared up considerably at night."

And in between;

"Don't be too hard on them Flo. They didn't mean any harm."

"I know that. Lionel is such a nice quiet boy and well mannered. But things – how shall I put it – have livened up so since Jim came on the scene."

"Thank goodness for that I say. Jim gives me quite a run for my money at crib. And Lionel is all the better for having company of his own age."

"I still say their mothers wouldn't like what they've done."

"You're forgetting Flo – Lionel himself told us that his mother died some years ago. His dad's sister keeps house for them now."

"Yes, of course, you're right. I'm sorry. Tall and polite though he is, Lionel does look as though he needs some proper mothering." Flo's voice had softened. But she still meant to have the last word.

"I'm sure they'll both have more respect now for other people's belongings."

"I'm sure you're right dear."

The old sailor leaned back in his chair knowing the squall to have blown itself out.

*

These were long nights or, to be accurate, very long blackout evenings during November and December 1939. Most of them were passed in the small but always warm, always cosy, living room. First a spot of homework. The bedroom, just like at home, was far too shivery for a rough, even very rough translation into French of,

"In wintertime light the dining room fire but two minutes before dinner is served up, in order that your master may see how saving you are of his coals."

Directions to Servants: Dean Swift. (Quotation Source)

In such icy conditions even Beaumarchais' *Le Barbier de Séville* (read in French in wintry Stroud) lost some of his zest for this, that and the other.

"Game of chess Syd?"

"OK Alf."

The chess board was fished out from behind the solid, highly polished sideboard and placed on the square dining table. Wooden chessmen were tumbled from their Oxo cube tin barracks and set in place – on an old pastry board loaned by Ma Appleton, and marked into appropriate squares, with chalk, by Jim.

In one corner of the room, close to the fireplace, sat 'Ma' – in a wooden armed easy chair, her flowered, white edged pinny smoothed down – a folded newspaper across her knees. She smiled a gentle smile and adjusted the round glasses on her longish nose.

At the table, but to one side of the players sat 'Pa' on an upright dining chair. He had removed his collar and loosened the front stud of his shirt. Over his long sleeved sweater he wore an unbuttoned waistcoat. His specs, their side-pieces neatly crossed, lay on the table.

The reflected dancing firelight glinted and sparkled in Ma Appleton's round glasses, in the cut-glass bowl and gleaming brass handbell (symbol and tool of caretaking), standing authoritatively on the sideboard.

Jim sat studying the opposing pawns, wondering what Syd's opening move might be this time – probably the 'Sherbert Herbert' again – or some variation of it. Over his pale grey flannel shirt with the faint red stripe, Jim was wearing his new grey pullover, a V neck again, with black and yellow edging. His brown hair, cut short, showed his 'bump of knowledge' (his mother's term for the back of his head which did stick out a bit) – to advantage.

But he still remained unsure about the value of his recently introduced 'kiss-curl', a quite pronounced curving hook of thick strands which looped above his right eyebrow.

While kissing had not been banned or rationed for 'the duration,' he had not sought, since the bust-up with Mary, either pecks or plonkers or * * * s of any kind. 'Was he fated,' he wondered, 'to be a one gal guy – or was he simply lacking in enterprise, or worse, just plain scared of being hurt again?'

"Right lads, let battle commence."

Pa looked at Syd, clad much as Jim, but far better looking with regular features, no twisted tooth and a mop of naturally curly, black hair. Being quiet and unassertive, he appeared quite unaware of the physical advantages he possessed. In this respect, he was totally the opposite of Ken.

Quite often this jolly party of four became a jollier one of five – and a jollier still when the numbers swelled to seven.

The doorbell rang.

"Come in lad. Sit yourself down."

The naturally generous and sociable Appletons were very ready to welcome the hapless 'Chub' into their small family circle. So were Syd and Alf, for an extra hand at crib and whist – or dominoes – or bagatelle meant more fun and more laughs. Besides, they felt sorry for the stocky lad with slicked back fair hair, billeted on his own with zealous Baptists.

"Don't know how he sticks it where he is. I couldn't or wouldn't," confided Jim to his diary.

Chub joined the card school, partly as an escape from the Bible-bashers but also to reassure himself that a world of innocent 'sin' was still alive and well. With evident delight he enrolled in this free and easy night school.

Periodically, the Appleton's married son, Donald, a local factory manager, would drop in, accompanied by his vivacious, pretty, and pert humoured wife, Pauline.

Pauline would come straight to the very feminine point.

"Well, and how do you boys like the girls in Stroud?"

Syd blushed and Alf mumbled;

"We don't know any."

"Well, you are a couple of slow coaches, I must say. I thought Syd at least, would have had plenty of admirers by this time."

Pauline looked pointedly at the lack lustre Romeo and raised her eyes archly to his curls.

Syd blushed again.

"And I suppose you'll tell me young Alf, if I can get it out of you, that you've got a girl in Birmingham. As if there were any pretty girls there. Come on now, spill the beans." Jim writhed but said nothing.

"Oh do stop teasing them Pauline. Let them get on with their game of crib."

Ma Appleton took no part in the mysterious rites of 'fifteen – two, fifteen – four...' but when her husband became excited and broke into a distressing coughing fit, she looked up anxiously from her reading;

"Don't overdo it Pa. You know what the doctor said."

*

Not for the first time, spritely Pauline had set off a disturbing train of thought. Attractive, quick-witted and secure in her status as a young married woman (which implied vast experience to callow youths), the Brummagem greenhorns became easy targets for her teasing darts of humour.

'But she did have a good point,' conceded Jim – reverting to his Hamlet role, as he lay awake in bed, vaguely aware of the muffled bouts of coughing from Pa and Ma Appleton's bedroom.

Beside him stretched the long form of Syd. Lucky devil, he was sound asleep – seemingly unperturbed by conundrums posed by the wiles of wenches. Still he'd most likely cop out one day. Pauline wasn't the only one to have eyed his curls with obvious approval. That bright young thing at Peckhams, the photographers, smiled winsomly at him each time he entered the shop. Keen photographer though he genuinely was, Syd seemed, just recently, to be popping into Peckhams far more often than his hobby required – and obviously, not always comfortably in Jim's company. Ah well, for the next 'development' (ho! ho!) Jim would do the decent thing and stay away.

'Come now,' he admonished himself, 'revenons á nos moutons. Was he really a one gal guy? There had been Brenda of Babbacombe of course with her habit of buying him ties. But did she really count, given the surrounding intrigue of which he was only partly aware?'

So far, he hadn't seen many girls in Stroud and none had caught his eye. Did he really want feminine company of his own age group – and if he did, how would he set about finding it? He couldn't think there'd be any monkey-runs in the blackout – and he didn't fancy joining any church simply to become involved with its social activities. Besides, Stroud boys in general, and Marling School boys in particular, were likely to be hostile to poaching by townies. None of the possible plans seemed worth the candle – and anyway, he was enjoying himself as it was, free of emotional turmoil.

But then there was Mary, always Mary. Was she being true to him? Probably he would never know – she was a free agent and most decidedly a free spirit. Well, let's hope he would see her at Christmas, and holly, and mistletoe and...

The harsh clangour of the school-yard bell brought him to a sitting bolt upright position.

"Come on, Weary Willie and Tired Tim, it's morning school this week remember?"

So it was.

*

Occasionally, the cosy interwoven patterns of homework and sixth form 'play-school' were agreeably brightened by visits to the flicks, to the Gaumont for instance, "quite a decent little cinema", but obviously not in the same league as that first Odeon built in the country, still standing splendidly intact at Perry Barr. As for *The Mikado*: "colouring, costumes, acting and singing first class. Especially Koko". On another occasion – "great dancing by G.R. and F.A." was vastly admired "in *The story of Vernon and Irene Castle*." What a marvellous pair of dancers – all four of them!

Yes, on balance, it could fairly be said that the tiny part of the home front in which Jim was involved, was in stout heart. A little more grub in greater variety would be welcome of course, particularly now that food rationing was in the offing.

But although morale at School House was high, Jim was dimly aware that heartache and homesickness were probably being endured in quiet, lonely corners of the town. Being a senior boy, Jim was once detailed to welcome a young stranger to Stroud.

"Rain, rain, rain from a leaden sky. Had to receive an evacuee at the station. Waited till four then they rolled up in a car. Took them to Ebley and found kid's billet. Felt sorry for him. Bravely kept his tears back when he said goodbye to his father."

"Felt sorry for him"; quite an admission from a shaving senior in the Upper Sixth who normally affected lofty, or rather 5' 6½" disdain in the presence of 'inky fingered fags.'

*

Far away from Ebley, far away from Britain, too much British shipping was being sunk, bringing the prospect of rationing nearer and nearer. New war fronts were opening up. "Well Russia has started on Finland now. Wonder what the outcome of this action will be...lost faith in Russians after this." On the plus side, the German "pocket battleship", the *Graf Spee* was "shelled and chased by 3 British cruisers, *Ajax*, *Achilles* and *Exeter*" into Montevideo on the River Plate.

It seemed to Jim, that whatever, wherever tragic/heroic events occurred, the mundane happenings of life just kept on happening, and would probably keep on happening.

"Free morning but stopped in and did some English revision except for a few intervals when I played chess and draughts and dominoes with Chub and Syd."

Despite, or perhaps even because of this curious division between work and play, Jim's exam results, the ones he cared about, proved reasonable enough. Mr Wise, senior English master, thought that Doug and Jim might achieve a Distinction in English, while 'Simla' "...reckons I ought to go to University. Hope I can. It would be great." As for German – rather like the *Graf Spee* – scuttled – at 33%.

*

Travelling into Birmingham and through the city's grimy industrial suburbs, Jim experienced a sense of revulsion at the dirt and ugliness visible from either side of the train. He had almost forgotten how wretchedly squalid certain areas of Birmingham really were. And now he had new yardsticks of measurement – a clean and quiet country town, the beauty of the Slad Valley and Cranham Woods.

But in tree-lined Hutton Road – and certainly up Wood Lane and Handsworth Wood, affinities with the countryside seemed stronger. Trees apart, he was certainly "very happy to see Mom and Dad again" and his uncles and Grandad seemed glad to see him. In fact, "Grandad gave me a shilling", a sum "unparalleled."

Jim's Christmas present arrived. Just as last year, not in a pillowcase; but this time with a difference, and what a difference. The present itself required a pillowcase being, "a modern super divan, a real smasher." Delivery of this "super divan" had to be taken through the front bedroom window – narrow, crooked staircases not being built with the manoeuvring of three quarter sized beds in mind.

So bucked was Jim by such a fine, brand new gift, that he walked airily to his Grandad's to play crib. "Beat Uncle Les!" So, the diligent application to certain extra mural studies in Stroud was paying off. A real triumph that, for Jim knew his Uncle Les wouldn't patronise his nephew by allowing him to win. The champion toppled at last. Yippee!

From Stroud, Jim had brought with him a present from Chub, a 1940 diary. "Silly ass. Wish he hadn't. Good diary and very grateful." It was quite a fat diary, a full page for each day except

Saturday and Sunday which had to share a page. Jim supposed that Chub had wanted to express his appreciation for the help given, in providing him with an oasis of fun in a dreary, text strewn Baptist desert. Without that gift, no record would have been kept, for better or for worse, of one impressionable lad's reactions to air raids – to the first week's pay packet – or to the complex problems posed by 'damsel delight'.

As he began to transfer essential data, like shoe size and hat size, from diary to diary, Jim glanced down the lists of books he had read, and films he had seen during 1939. Two writers featured prominently – P.G. Wodehouse and the American socialist, Upton Sinclair. Both received high praise – one for his Jeeves-Wooster humour and the other for his penetrating social analyses.

"The Wet Parade	Must get some more of his books exposing social wrongs. An excellent prohibition story.
The Metropolis	Good. Well written. Brings full force of vice of riches out. Extravagance well depicted.
They Call Me Carpenter	Vivid. Forceful. Very good guess of what might happen if Jesus Christ came on earth today."

To cope with the after effects of such sombre appraisals of some of the world's evils, P.G. Wodehouse's *Laughing Gas* provided a bracing pick me up.

With hopefully one more 1939 cinema visit to come, Jim checked that during the year he had been to the pictures some three dozen times. Only one film had he seen twice – first in October and again in December, a rattling good Western, *Stagecoach*, a real gent of a tough young cowboy that John Wayne. Jim's critical acumen, under the stimulus of sixth form teaching, was clearly on the move.

Then again, while he could still recall, with a chuckle or two, toothy George Formby plonking away on his ukulele in *Trouble Brewing*, he retained not the slightest recollection of what had happened in *Outlaws of Sonora*, starring the 'three Mesquetiers'.

Showing more maturity than usual, he forbore to exploit the puns possibly available to him among the mesquites.

*

"So what are you writing now, in that precious diary of yours?"

Jim looked across at his mom who had just 'come to' after 'resting her eyes for a bit.'

"Nothing much. Just a list of popular dance tunes for the year – one a month."

"So what have you got for October, my birthday month?"

""Run Rabbit Run.""

"That reminds me, would you like a rabbit stew if I can get a rabbit from Mr Smallmans?"

"You bet."

"What's the tune for your dad then?"

""Umbrella Man.""

Jim gave voice:

""He'll mend your umbrella

And go on his way...""

"Doesn't sound right for your dad – he can't even put a doorknob on straight when the screw's dropped out. And how about April – your month?"

""My own.""

"Yes, I like that – it's a pretty song. Deanna Durbin sings it beautifully."

Sal ventured a quavery quaver or two;

""Let me make you a part

Of the song in my heart.""

Sal smiled, leant back in her chair and rested her eyes again – but not for long.

"Jim?"

"Yes."

"Do you miss not being in Stroud?"

"In some ways."

"What ways?"

"Well, I miss the super hot bath I have each weekend – the hills, the lovely countryside, the interesting planes and things going on at

Minchinhampton aerodrome. Syd, Doug and I have been up there several times."

"What about when it's dark – you can't really get out then?"

"Luckily, Ma and Pa Appleton are great fans of *Bandwagon* on the radio – and, like I've told you, we play lots of card games. You needn't fret though – our homework always gets done on time."

"You haven't said much about football."

"I have played a few games but they've been pretty scratch affairs – one form against another. Marling play rugby. But we're hoping to play another Stroud school at football next term. I hope I get picked to play."

"But you *are* glad to be home again?"

"Yes, or course, most especially for Christmas – you know that well enough. Besides, no one I know can cook a lamb chop, or bacon and egg as well as you can."

Jim started to sing in a low voice;

" "Be it ever so humble,
There's no-o place like home." "

"I just hope there won't be any air raids on Brum while I'm in Stroud. That would really worry me. Are the Ridgeways still prepared to share their shelter with us?"

"Yes, thank goodness – and thank the Ridgeways. Have you finished the dance tune list?"

"Yes."

"So what's your favourite then?"

" 'Deep Purple' – I think, or maybe, 'South of the Border down Worcester town way.' "

Christmas Day morning and a warm sun shining, "...but what a difference between a fine day in Brum and a fine day in Stroud", even in the cheery company of old friends Dave and Bob. As twelve months before, the family card school reassembled at Uncle Sam's – some of its members looking rather tired, especially the uncles. Long hours on shift work in a blacked out factory, sapped resilience. Even so, "Great fun. Jolly company. Only lost 1½d."

By contrast, Boxing Day proved to be a bit of a frost, in every sense of the word. Having visited May's for one meal where young Bob was "bad, poor little kid"; Wilf, Sal and Jim walked to Ted's council house for the evening feast and revelries: "Dad's foot bad and

Mom with a corn. Like a funeral procession" for a sixteen year old lad, brimming with energy and pent-up excitement. But what a flop.

Ted had a bad cold, so had Roy, Jim's nephew. "What a lot!" A lively discussion... about the war, the Villa, the iniquities of the Capitalist system, the cunning of Uncle Joe Stalin... "alone livened up proceedings." Jim had enjoyed the peacetime 1938 celebrations far more, with the dance band music of Jack Hylton and Joe Loss setting the feet a tapping.

"You're a sweetheart,
If there ever was one ..."
and,
"I double dare you
to come over here...
And if that look in your eyes,
Means what I'm thinking of,
I double dare you
To fall in love with me,
I double dare you."
Great, just great.

Jim hardly dared think back to those heady days of 'seven times a kissing'.

*

After diary entries that did little credit to Jim's understanding that a fifteen year old girl, however personable, could not be a free agent when a family of five was planning its Christmas social programme, Mary and Jim met again after a separation of five yearning (at least on Jim's part) months.

"Nur wer die Sehnsucht kennt, weiss wie Ich leide."

(Byron didn't have all the best quotes – not by a long quill pen.)

*

"Hello Mary, It's lovely to see you again – especially after such a long time. I've missed you."

"Same here."

"Five months is much too long – even in wartime."

Shy, hesitant smiles were exchanged.

Mary had turned up 'on the dot' but Jim thought it prudent not to draw attention to the fact. And after all, it was the season of good will.

Mary looked a picture, a real, junior type cover girl in her new coat and shoes, a brightly coloured scarf about her neck, and sporting a perky little blue hat. Jim felt his heart racing madly. He longed to take the girl in his arms but was scared of making a false move. So, he kept his arms stiffly to his sides.

"So, how are you keeping? You look very well."

And so she did – her cheeks rosy, eyes sparkling from the cold air.

"Yes, I'm fine thank you – and glad to be in my own home for a few days. And how about you?"

Mary gave Jim a quizzical look.

"Oh, I'm all right thanks – and all the better for seeing you again."

"You look quite a bit older than when I saw you last."

"Nearly six months older and, to quote a phrase, there is a war on you know."

Mary laughed.

"Yes, everyone seems to make that an excuse now for anything that happens or doesn't happen. But you're now nearer seventeen than sixteen aren't you?"

"Yes – ageing rapidly."

"Sweet seventeen and...I'm surprised you've got the cheek to have that funny bit of hair across your forehead."

('Well, at least she had spotted the kiss curl,' thought Jim.)

"Has it attracted any peaches and cream country girls in Stroud?"

"Not that I've noticed. Still, I'm rather out of practice."

"Oh, at what?"

"Oh, at football, running – holding my mother's knitting – that sort of thing. But never mind all that. Tell me something about your new school and life in Worcester."

"Being with my aunt and uncle is like home from home in a way. But it takes time to settle into a new school, particularly a convent school."

"Too much religion?"

"No, not really, that's not it. Actually, I'm becoming rather interested in Catholicism. But the teachers are strict."

"Not too keen on tomboy pranks, eh?"

Mary smiled broadly, and the fencing dialogue continued – to be summarised later that day;

"Grand to see her again. She is no different except that she makes me want to like her more. Dressed very well. Looked radiant. Went a walk and had an interesting chat with her. What a girl. Going back to Worcester on Tuesday but I shall see her Monday. Yipee! Going to pictures. Hope to hold her hand. What a thrill again.

Saw Irene as well. She hasn't altered much" – still the same sensitive girl, with dark hair, dark and well defined eyebrows, perhaps slightly archer than before, after her recent experiences at a comptometer school. "She walks in beauty like the night..." It wasn't difficult to recall the stanza, and not just from that 1938 poetry reading. Jim had taken in Byron with his babyhood rusks.

*

On New Year's Eve, after setting himself free from the strangulating pressures of front and back studs, Jim settled down and wrote a broad brush review of global and personal affairs for 1939.

"A most eventful year...we are at war with Nazism and will continue to fight until we have crushed it for all time. At least that is what the politicians say. Sand in the futile eyes of mankind. War merely to prop up supports of Capitalism. Hope they fall. Hope the war soon ends. Caused too many privations and separations.

Become Senior Champion. Been evacuated. Had some marvellous experiences at Stroud. Something to remember in years to come. Have loved, lost, and found Mary. The only girl for me. Might laugh at these now expressed emotions later but sincerely hope not. She is a grand girl. Learnt to row but not to dance. Successful academic year. Hope to go to university if humanly possible. Shall do my best to repay Mom's and Dad's sacrifices for my education.

Feel very satisfied with 1939. Shall try to make 1940 better. Shall live every day with greatest energy."

Such a thwarting pity that just a week later food rationing had to be introduced;

Butter	4 oz	
Sugar	12 oz	
Bacon or ham – uncooked	4 oz	
Bacon or ham – cooked	3½ oz	per 'Jim' per week.

Chapter Twelve

What a Funny Kid I am

Jim hadn't long to wait outside the Villa Cross picture house on New Year's Day, 1940. Almost on time Mary arrived looking "grand", cheeks rosy again and bright hazel eyes sparkling from the cold air – and possibly (Jim thought) with incipient mischief.

"It's almost like old times," a tentative opener.

"Well, not quite."

"What do you mean?"

"Well, for one thing, you've not been playing football, and for another – you've now got that kiss curl which, to be honest, I don't much care for."

"Oh, that's a pity. I thought it might...er...er...help."

"I can't think in what way – and I'd like to snip it off."

"But if you did, I might lose all of my strength – or some of it anyway."

"Yes, I suppose that would be rather a pity."

Mary smiled, a touch roguishly, Jim believed, looking still for signs of encouragement.

Mary smiled again – this time rather sweetly.

"Come on, you old chump, it's time we went in," she tucked an arm inside his and gently pushed him up the steps towards the cinema doors.

Although Jim later evaluated *The Sun Never Sets* as a "quite good depiction of struggle between love and duty" (and he had had sharp experience of such a trial back in '38) his attention had repeatedly wandered away from the stirring adventures of Doug Fairbanks Jnr and Basil Rathbone, a pair of enviably handsome devils, to the girl by his side.

Whenever the slightly flickering images on the screen brightened, he took a cautious peep at his charmer's profile – at the well-formed eyebrow (no film star pencil-thin nonsense) straight nose, well-shaped, well-proportioned and inviting lips, the firm chin of a strong character. He reached across to take hold of her hand. Mary evaded his cautious move, still looking at the screen.

"Wouldn't let me hold her hands. Kept her gloves on. Wonder why."

Deep down perhaps, Jim sensed that a close personal relationship could not, unlike a piece of knitting, be picked up again, in just the same condition, all stitches just where they should be. K.2 tog. was far simpler, and needed far less patience than soothing hurt feelings, preventing further hurt, and re-kindling damped down emotions. So, no hand holding this time. Jim hadn't persisted.

Still, "OK afterwards though for she allowed me to kiss her goodbye."

Such quivering poignancy in wartime parting kisses.

When you thought about it, Shakespeare truly was 'the man for all seasons' for an apt quotation, if you knew where to look. Jim had remembered a suitable sentiment from one of the sixth form set books, *Coriolanus*.

"O a kiss long as my exile...and my true lip hath virgin'd it e'er since."

Hope burgeoned once more – with thoughts of a possible bike ride from Stroud to Worcester for a bitter-sweet wartime tryst. However, as a sobering counter weight to castles in the air romancing, Jim remained rather glad he had prefaced his 1940 diary with a quotation, from a forgotten source, that had impressed him with its insight into the vagaries of the human heart.

"Happiness comes more from loving than being loved; and often when our affection seems wounded it is only our vanity bleeding. To love, and to be hurt often, and to love again – this is the brave and happy life."

Devilish hard precepts (Jim thought) to follow, even if accepted. He hoped he wouldn't be tested too often.

Before returning to Stroud, Jim, with an 'Auld Lang Syne' mood upon him, called on Ken who made him "most welcome. Seems to have reformed quite a lot. Hooray. I should still like him for my best pal. He was once." (With an undeclared rider – but no more monkey running thank you.)

Fewer boys than had gone home for Christmas caught the train back to Stroud. With evacuation not being compulsory and no air raids having occurred, HGS boys who stayed in Brum re-started their studies at George Dixon Grammar School. Jim had not the slightest wish to exchange the wide open spaces of the Cotswolds for the school in City Road, even if it was on the edge of Edg-bar-ston. Perish the thought.

But Jim and Syd were shaken and upset by what they found on their return to School House – a distressed and tearful Ma Appleton and a very sick Pa, suffering from a serious chest complaint, a legacy, most probably, of his tough, seafaring days. "Seems to be touch and go."

"I'm very sorry boys, but you might have to sleep in the armchairs tonight."

"Try not to worry Ma, we'll help you out as much as we can. You'll see."

To tone themselves up for the tasks ahead, the friends borrowed, on the very afternoon of their arrival, a toboggan. Together with Chub, still rejoicing in his liberation from religious dogma into a zealot free new billet, they "hurtled down slopes of Rodborough Hill."

But the boys' determination to help an overworked and caring substitute mother was genuine enough. Ma not only had her two young lodgers to look after, a seriously ill husband to tend and a home to run – but a school to keep clean, tidy and above all, well heated – for the January of 1940 was indeed savagely, savagely cold.

So the boys did the washing up – and "Syd made the cup chocolate. Not a bad effort." With some instructions and supervision, they graduated to stoking and tending the schools' boilers – and barrowing the coal from bunker to boilers. Mission accomplished – signal given, by hoisting "Syd's cap to top of the [school] flagpole."

Aching stokers' muscles (free of tattoos) could be, and were, luxuriantly relaxed in "a glorious hot bath" – a phrase liberally splashed about in the diaries during the Appleton period – especially on Saturdays.

*

"Crikey, it's cold."

Syd shivered and slapped his arms vigorously across his chest.

"What you need is Polly Peckham to keep you nice and warm."

"Silly ass!"

Jim just managed to dodge the snowball slung his way.

"But by crikey, you're right."

Jim blew hard on the tips of his gloved hands.

"It'll be all right tho' once we get going. But I hope Chub won't keep us hanging about."

Chub didn't. A few minutes later he slithered to a halt by his two friends, bicycle tires crunching on the crisp, partly frozen snow. Small clouds of vapour drifted about his face.

"Crikey, it's cold."

Agreement on the brass monkey nature of the weather having been so amicably achieved, the three sixth formers cycled off to Quedgeley, near Gloucester, on a 'nature trip'. The day before, Jim had sought and been given permission by Baggy for the three of them to miss the boring school organised shower, and even more boring walk, in order to attend a blood tingling meeting of a fox hunt.

Arriving at Quedgeley, the trio found that the meet had been cancelled, doubtless due to the weather. Nothing else for it but to 'lark about'. Of the three, Jim tended to be the moving spirit when 'larking about' appeared on the agenda. Syd would never initiate a jape but would join in, as much out of good nature as interest, if others gave a lead. Or, as an amused spectator, with arms folded at mid-riff level, he would rock forwards and back with bubbling, near silent mirth, when, for example, Doug and Jim hurled bits of chalk, and cheerful insults, at one another in the form room.

Chub, a touch dour by temperament, tended to stay in the background.

With no picturesque hunt to capture, Syd, a keen photographer, trained his camera on his pals. At his own suggestion (rather a wizard wheeze really) Jim sat in an abandoned wooden wheelbarrow as Chub raised the handles.

The wheeze lay in the fact that the friends were positioned under a signpost pointing to the Bristol Road. "Can cross out road and substitute some [mileage] figure" – just as a lark and to indicate the arduous nature of the heroic task undertaken by Chub, who stood

looking suitably serious for his burdened with 'responsibility' role.
Jim, sitting in state, gave a cheery grin and a thumb's up sign. Click.

Figures, barrow, snow, post – all turned out fine. But Syd, later
to become an RAF navigator/observer – missed the finger part of the
post. Collapse of schoolboy joke. Months later, the sign itself went
missing when anti-invasion measures were introduced.

On to the River Severn then – and on the Severn for Jim, as the
river, still quite wide in its upper reaches, was frozen, bank to bank.
Tentatively, Jim stepped on to the mottled greys of the ice, ridged
here and there, lightly covered in parts with wind drifted snow.
Slowly, cautiously, a little fearfully, he made his way, in a series of
slanting moves, to the centre of the river. For this slithery expedition,
Jim was rigged out in the manner dear to the heart of the traditional
British amateur explorer.

From a broken tree branch he had fashioned a rough pole – thank
goodness, he always carried a penknife. He wore a long, i.e. just
below knee length grey raincoat, so much used that it never became
bone dry; shabby, second hand black galoshes over his shoes – and
cycle clips fastening his trousers just above the ankle. Standing on the
bank, Syd successfully recorded this escapade – without a tremor.
Maybe, he, like Jim, held his breath more than once.

What a day! What a half day, to be exact! To thaw out from the
morning's activities the lads later went to the Ritz and, "...saw *Beau
Geste* twice through". Plenty of hot action and blood stirring heroics
there.

*

The winter of 1940 was proving to be the hardest of the century –
to that time. For the first occasion since 1888 the Thames froze.
Protracted frosts and heavy snowfalls severely disrupted traffic and
communications.

But at the right time and in the right mix, a combination of ice,
snow and frost can be enchanting – a flawless crystalline joy.

"As it was so fine and clear in the evening went running to Star
Inn, up Slad Road and back. Great running along frosty, snowy roads
in moonlight. Kept quite a good pace. Syd on his bike paced me.
Feel very fit now."

In that sharp, crisp, nose-nipping air, thick pristine snow massed on cottages, farms and fields; thin clouds slipping across the moon; Jim experienced an exhilarating sense of physical well-being. He would readily have taken on not only Jimmy Lester, but his hero Sidney Wooderson as well – had they all happened to meet up on the frozen snow of Slad Road. What a cross country race that would have been!

But, slither and slide back to School House – another letter to write.

As he scratched away with his Conway-Stewart 'Dinky' fountain pen, Jim wondered if roughly four months of war had seen the sales of postage stamps shoot up. He thought it likely, given the myriad separations that war had already brought about, with no doubt many more to come. Until evacuation, he had had little occasion to write to his dad – a postcard from Babbacombe – but now, things were very different.

"Dear Dad,
Many thanks for letter containing a mine of philosophical wealth, and also material wealth which is far more useful." (Little point in beating about the bush. His dad could be rather prosy, polemical, pontifical. A touch florid too – Byron's influence at work again. And a 1/6d postal order really was a boon.) "Now I can go to a big Boxing Tournament which is to be held in the Liberal Hall..." (Such events surely came within the definition of a broad based (maybe base over apex) education?) "...Mr Appleton got up today. The first time in five weeks. Pretty weak on his pins."

And so were some of the boxers a few evenings later. "Several good scraps, three knock-outs. One chap went through the ropes. What a tough crowd watch boxing matches. Interesting survey of human nature could be made from their faces. All characters."

Including the only HGS boy who seemed to be present?

He thought about Mary and the time he had taken her into the boxing booth at the Onion Fair. Would he have brought her to the Liberal Hall? Decidedly not, given the appearance, language and behaviour of some of the plug-uglies raucously cheering and jeering nearby.

Despite the atrocious, transport clogging weather conditions, letters arrived regularly from home, some containing life-saving postal orders – and usually a Birmingham weather report. At the end of January heavy snows returned. Dave wrote to say that it had been snowing for a whole 48 hours. No bread deliveries said Dad. Golly, things must really be tough if the Birmingham Co-op roundsman couldn't get round. Jim sniggered – how would that poor widow woman, the one with the lovely pair of china dogs get on? Golly, Christmas 1938 already seemed a lifetime away. Then, he hadn't even heard of Stroud, and now he was thoroughly at home there.

In his last letter Dad had also given his son advice "not to have *War Illustrated* bound. Considered the matter carefully and decided he is right. In any case it would cost 10/- to have them bound in the deluxe edition, the one which I wanted."

Having made that well-calculated choice, Jim picked up a recent copy of the relatively new magazine, *Picture Post*, a bit pricey at 3d but featuring some wonderful photography. Jim looked at two old jossers, seemingly much the same age as his dad, who appeared smiling and beribboned on the front cover. "Back on the Job. Men of the Home Defence Battalions (see pages 40-43)."

Jim turned to those pages, lavishly illustrated with photos of ex-soldiers who had put on khaki once again "to guard vital points on the home front." It seemed impossibly weird to think of Nazi soldiers, storm-troopers perhaps, fighting their way maybe to Minchinhampton aerodrome. Jim shivered and turned to the first in a new series of articles on "How I would Run the War" – this one by Mr H. Wickham Steed.

And who was Wickham Steed when he was out? Obviously a toff from his name. "A former editor of *The Times*..." Oh, *The Times* – 'nuff said. Pro-appeasement and anti-Labour, that lot. Jim hadn't forgotten that Tory rag's stance on the Spanish Civil War, from that historic debate at school – oh, way back.

Jim promptly turned back to something that had earlier gladdened his eyes, "The Swirl of the Can-Can". A nifty looking lot of girls there, a jolly sight chirpier in appearance than the miserable, care-worn lady in the 'Wincarnis' advert.

"Women's Struggle to Keep Going

Is wartime slowly sapping your vitality?

Almost every woman is in real need of a wartime pick-me-up..."

At, "...only 6/6 & 3/9" a bottle. Only!

Blimey, at those prices the menfolk of such jaded ladies would soon be called upon to sacrifice their beer and baccy money. And the war not six months old!

Jim returned to re-reading a cheery letter recently received from a totally unjaded, completely chirpy young lady. But, hang on a minute. Was Mary *his* young lady once more? Since that 'long as my exile' kiss she had been writing to Jim. Naturally, not so promptly or as frequently as the impatient would be lover again, wished. In fact, his diary entries yo-yo'd in sentiment from unjust scorn, "Scatterbrain Mary", to soaring elation.

"You're as pleasant as the morning,
As refreshing as the rain,
Isn't it a pity that you're
Such a scatterbrain.

When you smile it's so delightful,
When you talk it's so insane..."

No, that last line certainly wasn't justified in this case. True, Mary could be irritatingly vague on some matters – and yet quite specific on others. All part of the feminine make up Jim supposed. Still, it was useful to know, in reply to a question prompted by that fragrant last Villa Cross meeting, that, "She uses 'June' perfume. Wants me to buy her some! We'll see. We'll see."

Thursday, 8th February, "Crept half afraid downstairs this morning. Saw to my greatest delight...a letter from Mary." She made suggestions for a possible meeting and added, "PS I don't know whether you know it, but I like you very much."

"Je suis aux anges," was Jim's cultured reaction.

"Shall have to send her a Valentine now. What a funny kid I am. How my moods change. Shall have to keep referring to the quotation in front of diary."

Maybe he did. But on that particular joyful day, he certainly larked about later in the library "with water pistols." Tut, tut, such juvenile behaviour might have been expected from a Dickie but surely not from a senior prefect coming up to seventeen. A fig for orthodox thought – even short back and sides hair had to be let down occasionally. And anyway, the water was clean and kept away from the books.

In brief, Jim was now enjoying a whale of a time – finding his feet on the river Severn, sliding about on Stroud's ice bound canal, organising a scratch game of very rough and partly ready ice hockey, watching bruisers thump one another, keeping the 'home (school) fires burning', playing a quiet, slow-paced game of crib with the recuperating Pa Appleton, nimbly back chatting with quick-witted Pauline. Even being "bandaged up all over the place" by Pauline's husband Donald was a lark.

Nothing melodramatic about the swaddling – no jealous young husband situation, no assault or battery – simply a 'test run' for the following day's First Aid Exam Donald was due to take.

Stretched out on a camp bed, Jim vaguely wondered how the two women in his life might react to his semi-mummified appearance. His mother, "a grand little woman" would have been fearful and compassionate. And Mary? She would have laughed, prodded firmly here and there, a mock serious expression on her face, and probably checked the bandages for effectiveness and neatness. Mary had expressed hopes to become a nurse one day.

Carefree days – perhaps the most carefree of Jim's life so far – despite the war, despite his own erratic changes of mood. But again he recognised, if only briefly and occasionally, that other boys, especially the younger ones, might find evacuation tough going. That kid he had escorted to Ebley for example. Even Dickie, cheeky little devil though he was, seemed to have been through a bad patch. But "he appears to be settling down more, and becoming a little steadier. Good job." Jim, adopting a sort of older brother role, taught the young scallywag how to play chess. "Seems to have picked it up OK"

By this time, a recreation club had been established at a Church Institute, open every morning for "chess, games, table tennis etc. Hot milk. For boys who have free morning." Jim "popped along" to check it out. "New idea of Head's. Good one for once." Not a glowing tribute – but, in its particular context, – a warm seal of approval from a sixth form sophisticate.

Whatever the peaks and troughs of experiences during, say a month, in Stroud, the 'proper 'umdrum' (Arthur Askey's catch phrase from the immensely popular radio programme – *Bandwagon*) summed up much of daily life. Went to school, did homework, listened to radio. 'I thang you' – Arthur again. An occasional variation, but still on the 'umdrum side; "went to barbers. Had a jolly good haircut but didn't he take an unconscionable long time about it. Maddeningly slow." 'Twas ever the way of barbers: snip snip chat chat snip snip; chat chat chat.

Now there was an impressive, imposing word for you – 'unconscionable'. Jim resolved to work it into some essay or other – perhaps one on *Hamlet* (his favourite set book). A possible sentence began to form itself in his mind. 'In the opinion of some distinguished critics, Hamlet, although a man of exquisite conscience and sensibility, took an unconscionable long time to make up his mind.' ('Rather like a lady choosing a pair of shoes or a new hat,' thought Jim. 'No, better leave that bit out; not quite at the same august level as wondering when to kill your stepfather.')

But how did teachers set about marking work fairly and consistently? Earlier that term, Jim had tried an experiment, successfully as he saw it; "Improving in my French proses. Now that I give mine in last I get a much better and fairer comment."

During that dull day when 'Le Barbier de Stroudville' was at his garrulous worst, Jim showed startling, romantic enterprise.

"Bought a Valentine for Mary", not only bought it but sent it and not only sent it, but put a billet doux style letter in besides.

Next day, a dive into a deep trough.

"Mr Appleton touch and go again. Much worse than last time. Doctor and nurse been. Not much hope...He says the funniest wildest things. Lightheaded."

The hard decision could be put off no longer. Syd and Alf would have to be transferred from fire-stoking duties. "Great pity for we were very comfortable and happy here."

The friends called at the Billetting Office on Monday, were told to call again on Wednesday, when they would be informed where their new billet would be, and on Friday they would move in. Simple and efficient. No fuss. The boys had no direct influence on how such decisions were made. They took what they were given. They vaguely wondered whether the matching of supply and demand within the local community was a tricky business, and rather supposed that it could well be so. Come to think of it, had anyone ever replaced Chub at the Bible-bashers? Well, they had escaped that 'posting' thanks perhaps to the idol of the minor molar, exercising his benign influence from deep within his Birmingham tea-chest temple.

*

"Hey Syd, have you seen this latest batch of *Picture Posts* that Pauline brought for Pa?"

"No, I'll have a gander later on when I've finished with my *Amateur Photographer*."

"There's an article here that might interest you."

"Oh, and what's that?"

"How to photograph a – Beauty."

"And who's the beauty?"

"Hang on a mo! Wow! Great Scott! For a minute I thought it was Polly Peckham. But it's Diana Churchill."

"You silly ass."

"Will you be popping into Peckhams tomorrow?"

"I might."

"If you do, just ask Polly if she knows anything about a perfume called 'June'."

"And why should I do that?"

Jim pondered.

"No, better not. She might get the impression that you were planning to buy her some."

"Ass."

There was a rustle of pages being turned.

"These A.T.S. girls look a bit of all right."

Syd made no comment.

"I said these A.T.S. girls look a bit of all right."

"I heard you."

"Do you think you'll join the RAF Syd?"

"I may do."

"You'd look better in blue as a Brylcreem boy."

"Don't be such a twerp."

"Your dad was in the artillery in the Great War wasn't he?"

"Yes, he was."

"I hope you don't mind my saying this, but when I first met him, I noticed that one arm was bent in a funny way and that he wore a leather glove on one hand."

"Yes, he was wounded in France and suffered some bad burns."

"I'm sorry."

Both lads fell silent for a few minutes, assailed by sombre thoughts.

"Things are beginning to look pretty bad for the Finns aren't they?"

"And things will begin to look pretty bad for Sunny Jim if he doesn't shut up for a bit. Why've you suddenly become such a chatterbox?"

"I suppose I'm a bit het up about changing our billets. I just hope we don't have to undergo Chub's kind of baptism."

"I'm with you there – but now shut up will you. And no more cracks about Polly."

'Golly,' thought Jim, 'best back off with the teasing, at least for a bit.'

*

After that depressing trough of the imminent break up of the great good fellowship cribbage club – a modest peak – the resumption of football. But "...the ground as hard as iron, ball bouncing everywhere except the right place." As Jim had told his mom at Christmas, games of football, so far, hadn't been up to much. With Marling a rugby playing school, HGS lads had been restricted to inter-form matches, usually one hour a week, "good game but they [the Shell] had fourteen men. Seemed to be everywhere." Even the sixth formers with their superior intellect were forced to yield to the grubby many headed. Lackaday.

After that modest rise in good fortune, signalled by the resumption of football – a veritable Everest – a letter from Mary, brimming with affection. It might justly be called a love letter. Jim's Valentine had 'thrilled her to bits.' "Sweetest thing I could have done. She can see me in a fortnight's time. Dying to see me. No longer 'dear Jim' but 'dearest.' Yipee! Again je suis aux anges except that we have to move tomorrow."

It was all very well being emotionally 'aux anges' but human muscle and sinew aux bras, aux jambes et au dos – were needed for the trudge along the London Road in the direction of Cirencester, carrying schoolboy goods and chattels. From the outside, Stafford

House seemed solid, square, imposing, set on the edge of open countryside.

Alf knocked. The heavy wooden door swung open.

"Mrs Jenkinson did not seem too friendly, but I think she was a little ill at ease."

"I'm afraid the Captain can't see you today. He's a little seedy. But bring your luggage in," she said.

Syd and Alf stared blankly at one another. 'A little seedy'? What *did* the well-groomed, prim-looking person mean – a lady obviously from her bearing and cut glass voice. Irreverent images of Uncle Les's budgies came fluttering to Jim's minds eye. Memsahib was right up to a point. Although the boys saw and heard the Captain (army retired) they were not introduced to the red-faced man with the "Bai Jovian accent...probably fond of his whisky."

Jim dumped his suitcases in "our bedroom, quite nice" and then returned to Brum, for it was half term break.

Chapter Thirteen
Three Billets

"Just take your Dad's tool box will you Jim, and see if you can fix the lavatory pipe. It may need a good wallop."

From the back of the pantry, where the hardened earth floor remained uncovered by lino, Jim picked up a battered old wooden box, its lid partly split, one hinge broken: a badly discoloured and scarred box containing assorted hammers, a bent screwdriver – and a rusty bradawl with part of its handle missing, a handful of assorted nails. Oh, and a pair of pincers.

With schoolboy delight, and vastly more vigour than skill, Jim knocked up the lead pipe and the gushing water ceased to cascade down the flaking, white-washed wall of the dangerously chilly reading room.

Jim slid and slithered back to the warm, almost stuffy living room and began browsing through back numbers of his *The War Illustrated*.

"Convoys are safe with the Royal Navy" – quite the right thing to say for morale maintaining purposes, but how well did the claim match the reality Jim wondered.

"How to Tell Non-Commissioned Ranks of the Forces." Jim looked keenly at the illustrations displayed under "Petty Officers of the Royal Navy." Given recent experiences in Stroud, would he be off to a flying start to become "Chief Stoker"? Unlikely, he thought, and he would definitely rule himself out of the promotion stakes if tattooing was involved!

"Once Again the Stern Vow" – Jim looked at the French soldiers grouped "in front of a concrete pill box on the Western Front", hoar frosted grass and earth above their helmeted heads. Chalked defiantly on the front of the pillbox, in large clear letters, the historic words, 'On ne passe pas'. "'They shall not pass.' This was the motto that inspired the heroic defenders of the fortress of Verdun, whose amazing stand against the Kaiser's hordes was one of the most glorious feats of arms in the history of the French Army."

But would Adolf's mechanised hordes fight that kind of World War I frontal battle? Jim still retained uneasy thoughts about that article he had read in *Illustrated* which implied that Hitler might well by-pass the Maginot Line by tackling the weaker defences of Belgium and Holland. Ah well, sufficient unto the day...

Jim yawned, stretching his arms above his head. He wasn't bored, just sleepy. Soon be time to put up the blackout shutters to the living room and kitchen windows. Good old Bill. For his in-laws, he had built two lightweight frames of thin strips of wood, and covered these with a sort of tar paper. The frames were held in place by swivelling metal catches. Clever chap, Bill – and a good laugh. 'Go' blimey ah!' – to borrow his catchphrase.

So much that was routine these days, thought Jim. Putting up the blackout – putting on the kettle – putting a brave face on 'things.' He glanced affectionately towards his mother, still sat in her old arm chair – still clicking steadily away with four pointed, steel needles. Socks for Pop, socks for Son, socks for lads in the forces, socks for the entire allied armies, so it seemed.

Wilf, though cheerful, was quieter than in pre-evacuation days, thinking perhaps about Alec on the *Ark Royal* and about Phil somewhere in France. Wilf was also often dog tired, what with food rationing, the blackout, the cruel weather – and his so far fruitless search after a job. Wilf regarded himself as being perfectly capable of carrying out say, the duties of a night-watchman at a factory engaged on war work.

But with his gammy leg and the bitter, arctic conditions, it was hard enough to keep his balance just going to the lav and back, let alone taking a calculated risk with each swing of that stiff leg, as he slowly, awkwardly, picked his way along the treacherously slippery streets. It would certainly take much more than a 6/6 bottle of Wincarnis to replace the chilling misery of standing at a bus stop in blasting icy winds, with a warm glow of contentment.

Snow still lay stretched in large, unlovely, dirtied mounds down each side of the roads, and soon everywhere was "terribly slushy and dirty underfoot." Handsworth Park pool remained frozen and the boathouse roof had collapsed under the sheer weight of snow.

After four nights blissful sleep on his "old divan" (now all of seven weeks 'antiquity') Jim was quite ready to return to the fresh country air of Stroud, especially with his extra pocket money – half a crown from Uncle Les and a couple of bob from Uncle Harold. Besides, he was curious to see how Sydney had got on. Had the seedy, light duties only, Captain recovered and spoken to him yet?

By happy chance (or had Syd been looking out for him?) the friends met at the gate of Stafford House.

"Wotcher Alf."

"Wotcher Syd."

"Things all right at home?"

"Not too bad, thanks. There's still bags of snow about. The park pool's frozen and the boathouse roof has fallen in under the weight of snow. Our lavatory pipe had burst but I managed to fix it. How's tricks here? How've you been getting on?"

"Not so dusty. But I'm glad you're back."

"Why, what's up? Is the Cap *still* a little seedy?"

"I can't really tell. He hardly says anything. More pickled than seedy, I shouldn't wonder. But best mind your ps and qs."

"Right."

"And your ks, fs, and ss."

"Crikey, what are they?"

"Knives, forks and spoons. You'll see."

Jim later recorded, "Dinner ready when I got in. Beautiful dining room. Lace mats, serviettes. Silver plate everywhere. Huge sideboards. Everything bright and lustrous. This certainly is a high class billet and they certainly don't starve."

No, they certainly didn't. Come to think of it though, reasoned Jim, the term 'middle class' never did seem to be linked with 'malnutrition' did it? Odd, though, the Cap and his missis could surely have afforded a tablecloth? Perhaps such people didn't drop crumbs? In peacetime, this couple had probably employed servants to relieve them of such unutterably tedious considerations. In his imagination, Jim could almost sense a tall, turbaned fellow appearing silently at his elbow, to remove his empty soup plate. (He really had tried hard, had Jim – and every potential slurp had been successfully suppressed.)

Had Syd and he entered the land of the lotus eaters? Jim wondered – and watched, dredging his memory for all that he could recall about table manners, and covertly watching for clues as to how to tackle the cutlery.

The Cap, with bloated, mottled red face, sat at the head of the table. At the far end, and opposite to her husband sat Mrs Cap, "a grand cook."

Syd and Alf were posted, exactly midway, along opposite sides of the table – Jim to the right of the Cap.

By raising his left hand to his left temple, Jim could and did wink surreptitiously with his left eye – at his friend. With admirable self-restraint, Syd just avoided the social catastrophe of choking on the 'delicious oxtail Mrs Jenkinson.'

Apart from the normal courtesies associated with the circulation of the condiments – and such like, there was no conversation at the table.

Mrs Cap darted frequent anxious glances at her husband as if fearful of an imminent explosion. A tinge of puce suffusing the mottles might signify red alert. Allowance had to be made for the Cap. He had probably never dined before with a couple of lads who would be over promoted if they ever made corporal. 'Gad, the Empah really was going to pot.'

But what the social atmosphere lacked in warmth of feeling and genuine, as distinct from ritual, hospitality, was, to some extent, off-set by creature comforts: a "hot brick wrapped in flannel and placed in bed at night", as well as the ready availability of "a lovely hot bath" and not just on Saturday nights.

Outside the house, stretched an extensive garden with a stream flowing past at the far end. Nearby, another stream, a canal, the railway line "and plenty of fields and dales to roam in".

The Cap who "drinks whisky like water and smokes cigarettes by the dozen" spent much of his severely rationed active time in the garden, with its "well laid out flower beds – wheeling barrow loads of muck about." Jim completed his careful inventory by noting – an orchard and twenty-six fowl – not just a 'couple of dozen' – but twenty-six. Had there been one of the compilers of the Doomsday Book among his forebears? He set off to count the fruit trees.

The Sunday of 'Operation Bicycle Clips' neared. Preparations began. "Borrowed a thermos...had my haircut. Less weight to carry. Bought some pop and chocolate...shall have to get up at six."

Sunday arrived. "Lovely riding through the dawn" through a countryside about to stir after the numbing, savage shock of winter's onslaught. With a light heart, Jim went bowling along through Gloucester, Tewkesbury and northwards on the A38 to Severn Stoke, some six or seven miles south of Worcester – "a pretty little place" where a pretty young girl soon arrived, almost on time. (The timing of such journeys could not be judged to a nicety).

"Hello again. You're looking very well."

"Good morning – and so are you. I hope you've not been waiting long?"

"Just long enough to get my breath back and straighten my tie."

Mary really did look 'a treat' in a warm orangey brown skirt and jacket; brown hair fluffed out by the breeze, cheeks a healthy pink, from cycling, and, Jim hoped, perhaps just a little bit from excitement. He stood quietly, lost in admiration, and lost for words.

"Did you have a good journey?"

There was a pause.

"Oh – sorry – I was dreaming. Yes thanks – and you?"

"Fine thank you. Well then, where shall we go?"

"As it's still a bit chilly, how about if we go a short cycle ride, park the bikes somewhere safe and then go for a walk before we have our sandwiches?"

"Sounds fine."

They cycled slowly, side by side, up and down a variety of quiet country lanes, keeping an eye open for a suitable barn or farm out-building that might be 'to let'.

"I notice you've got rid of your kiss curl. A good job too."

"Well, I thought it better to reduce the wind resistance for when I was cycling."

And so, a Sunday paced hour or two passed all too quickly by, under grey skies, the fields, trees and hedges seemingly stunned into damp drabness after winter's ferociously freezing attack. No buds were breaking yet, no glint of sunshine relieved the greyness.

Mary was certainly much quieter than usual, not subdued or unhappy but thoughtful, pre-occupied almost. She was clearly not in a high bantering or flirtatious mood, despite the earlier 'crack' about the kiss curl. Still, Jim was pleased just to be in her company, knowing now that girls had moods – and, after all Mary was now fifteen and a half which he believed could be a very moody age.

It was obvious if irksome, that today's mood was markedly different from that of the elated, ardent girl of not many days ago, who had written to tell him that she was 'thrilled to bits' and etc. with his Valentine card. But Jim now had sufficient experience and gumption to realise, that it was one thing to write with feeling in the warmth and privacy of a home, but quite another to warm up to a romantic interlude in that battered countryside, with frost damage everywhere evident. Certainly, it was chilly enough to warrant a cosy cuddle but the circumstances just weren't right.

Ah well, he was learning he hoped, that there were times to press forward and times to bide one's time, frustrating though that was. And he still entertained dark, unsettling suspicions that convent schooling might be curbing Mary's natural vivacity – if that was the word. But then school didn't last for ever.

As the youngsters parted, Jim gave Mary's hand an extra long squeeze, hoping she would thereby realise his deep yearning. She smiled, but made no remark.

They pedalled away in opposite directions, neither looking back.

'Dear Diary': Mary is "improving, if it's possible as she grows older...good to see her again. Hope to see her at Easter."

Along with the memories, the round trip of seventy miles on a sit up and beg bike, meant greater pleasure than ever in that evening's "lovely hot bath".

*

Next day, Jim was still fit enough for strenuous football – "pitch extremely muddy. Very tiring. But just the game and conditions I like. We won 4 – 1. And I scored two goals! First time I have scored for months and months, probably years." (Allowance to be made for schoolboy hyperbole, a common condition but soon outgrown.)

At long last, the projected match against a Stroud school (Stroud Central) was fixed. Jim, appointed captain, promptly went into a team selection huddle with "Baxter, Hudson and Grainger. Think we ought to win..." The right approach but wrong result – "lost 1 – 2". Match appraisal – "...nobody to blame. Our forwards could not finish off their good work, hesitating in front of goal." (Still the same old trouble that had dogged his entire football career, as seen by the left back – 'steady and forceful' or not.) "However, it was a rattling good game and I enjoyed it very much. Late for school but that of little importance." Nothing wrong with those priorities – and it was the turn, that week, of the HGS boys to attend school during the afternoons, including Saturday – a particular bind during the coming cricket season.

On the eve of this last match that Jim played for his school, he had, along with Syd, been served notice to quit by Mrs Cap.

She "told us...that her health was being impaired and that she could not stand the strain of extra work. What a lot of tommy rot. They never wanted us in the first place, so why not be honest about the whole thing."

Stafford House had been home for only a fortnight, out of which Jim had been in Brum for four days, in a real home. From the outset, the friends had sensed the Cap's attitude of – 'You're only here on sufferance.' He had probably barked at his wife – 'you wanted 'em, you get rid of 'em.'

Later, Jim was to learn from Memsahib that his dad had written what, in her view, was a very offensive letter to her husband – "expect it was about allowance for my keep." Jim rejoiced knowing that his dad was no man to be pushed around by anyone, least of all by toffee nosed toffs. Then again, what a difference in their snooty behaviour from that of Ma Appleton. Ma gave Jim "ten shillings which she maintains she owes Mom" for 'keep' paid for but cut short. Overall, the officers' mess approach to life stood in cold and unfavourable contrast with the homely, good fellowship experiences enjoyed within the 'other ranks' Appleton family circle.

But a plea of mitigation for the toffs was entered by Jim himself ('fair play's...and all that') – but only in specific terms for Memsahib. In the final days of the boys' stay, Memsahib tried to make them as comfortable as possible. Jim acknowledged as much to his diary. And after all, maybe Jim, quite unwittingly, had tipped the scales and pushed the Cap to push his wife to give their lodgers the push.

As part of the History course, Jim had been reading the 'Communist Manifesto', heaving sighs of relief when he had finished with its turgid prose. But the Manifesto's presence in Stafford House may well have had a deeply unsettling effect on the pukka sahib hosts. 'Good Gad – fancy harbouring a Brummagem Bolshie in their midst!'

*

But where next for these lads thrown out on their well-washed necks?

Enter dependable Baggy Brandon – senior French master. He and his wife were put in charge of a large empty house where the great unwanted – some forty to fifty boys eventually, were to stay.

Syd and Alf became two of a fourteen strong advance party of 'misfits' to occupy Northfield in the Uplands district of Stroud. Northfield was a fine building standing in a fair bit of land and close to open countryside. Address – Folly Lane. How ironically apt.

Jim's first reactions to his new home were mixed.

The other twelve lads he considered "not too bad a lot" – but hoped, vainly, that no more of the great unwashed and unloved would appear. He saw potential in the dining room for a table tennis tournament – and the neglected lawn tennis court could probably be knocked back into shape. Two greenhouses and a conservatory promised to bring out Syd's latent gardening skills, a born, slippered potterer and potter if ever there was one, good-natured Syd. In short, something for everyone, even a maid, for a while, for the amorous 'Chips' to ogle.

Jim settled down to some serious swotting, for after Easter he would be in his last term as a schoolboy with the HSC exams to tackle – and then what? Well, one step at a time.

He leaned back against a tree growing on top of a grassy bank which overlooked the tennis court. He gave a sigh of resignation and picked up *Le Pilote* – a set book. "A son réveil, Older trouva un temps gris, un vent qui soufflait avec hargne, et une mer, grise aussi..." Jim's thoughts drifted to other types of 'temps gris' – the period immediately following his bust-up with Mary, for instance. But 'hargne'? Hargneux(euse) – surly, peevish, cross-grained? That must be it – or did it mean sleet? Either way, pretty dreary that seascape, rather like his own life at times.

Jim looked up at the sound of war whoops – but only for a few seconds. Just 'Chips' and 'Hitler' (a boy with a very dark downy moustache) seeking to skewer one another again, with the long bamboo canes intended for runner beans. It was early March and although the real war hadn't fizzled out, hostilities had become relatively quiet, with the Russo-Finnish war almost at an end.

A few weeks earlier, Britain had been able to rejoice in the successful action carried out by *HMS Cossack*. This destroyer had rescued over three hundred British prisoners of war from the German tanker *Altmark* which had sought to evade capture in a Norwegian fjord. Then on 11th March, the day of Wilf's sixty-second birthday, butchers had become a mighty power in the land, and most particularly in every local community. Meat rationing, by price, was introduced. Housewives set to and honed their wheedling skills as they had never been honed before.

*

"What the dickens are you doing here?"

Jim was staggered. Having skimmed through the remaining chapters of *Le Pilote*, he had returned to his dorm (he was in charge of one, and Syd of another) to find young Dickie looking rather disconsolately out of the window. Dickie turned, trying to smile as he did so, "I've walked out of my old billet because they were treating me so badly. I've been told I can stay at Northfield – in your room. You don't mind do you?"

Jim reflected. The 'cheeky young devil's' features, troubled now, did so remind him of Mary's, especially the large eyes and defiant tilt of the chin.

"No, of course not. But just mind you don't play me up too much, otherwise you'll be well and truly scragged."

The boys exchanged broad grins – and a day or two later cycled together, with Syd to Cirencester. Jim had strengthened his Worcester connection and Dickie felt more secure in the 'boarding school' environment of Northfield. Not a bad outcome, all things considered.

"Are you going back to Worcester for Easter?"

"Yes, but Dad was talking about taking us for a holiday in Devon."

So that was why scatterbrain Mary had been so irritatingly vague in her last letter about a possible Easter re-union. "Tout comprendre c'est tout pardonner." Another 'pearl' he'd try to work into some exam answer or other. Jim resolved to pay more heed to such wisdom, in other ways as well – if he could remember in time. (Always leave yourself an escape route – another 'pearl'.) And emotions did so complicate matters.

*

While genuinely pleased, as always, to see his mom and dad, Jim had found coming into Brum by train "repulsive." The contrast between "clean open countryside with its frolicking lambs and shooting buds" and "the filth and grime, the squalor, the poverty, the 'sick hurry'" of the city was stark. "A pall of gloom like that of smoke over the city settled over our compartment as we drew nearer."

But the Matthew Arnold acolyte soon adjusted once more to familiar faces and familiar scenes – some of the latter now revealing grim additions, the anti-aircraft guns in Perry Park for instance. Old friendships were resumed – with Dave, with Bob – and later Ken. Relatively new activities were further developed, particularly rowing on park pools. But no girls caused a ripple, on any surface.

On Easter Monday, Dave and Jim, bemoaning the lack of feminine company, gave the zoo at Dudley, with its advanced design, the once-over. Extensive enclosures housed the big cats. Concrete platforms built into a steep hillside, allowed these majestic animals to bask – and to be seen without having to gawp through iron bars. "Extremely interesting and well set out zoo," seemed a fair judgement. But did the animals have air-raid shelters? Jim hoped so.

Sport attracted its due attention. On the first Saturday at home, Jim bought a pair of spiked running shoes, 10/6. Not cheap but well worth the price to have some clobber of one's very own. A pair of "abbreviated", quite racy, black shorts as well – not much material for 3/3. But they might come in handy if ever he joined The Birchfield Harriers as he hoped to do some day. The shorts were 'blooded', or rather, muddied, when he turned out for the Bridge Football Club against a factory team. After being 0 – 5 down, an honourable draw was achieved.

Soon, Jim was training again, but no sherry and no chérie this year, blast it. But good old Doug joined him – Doug, veteran friend from Crompton Road days and keen competitor from last year's sports. What an age ago that contest already seemed. And now, instead of being able to include more good red meat in his training diet for 1940, as earlier planned, Hitler had seen to it that Jim's intake of zip providing steak, was to be drastically reduced. The knock-on effects of war were truly incalculable.

So, steakless, back to Perry Playing Fields with 'good old Doug.'

"How exhilarating it is to go bounding along the springy turf with all the joy and carefreeness of youth." (If there wasn't such a word as 'carefreeness' then there jolly well should be.)

After the training runs – a highly evocative solitary walk "...by all appearances, they have ploughed up that field where Mary and I spent so many ecstatic evenings together. The clumsy rude boot of the farm labourer now desecrates that hallow'd and sacred spot." Wow!

The successful prosecution of a war, including the 'Dig for Victory' campaign, entailed many changes, some of a sacrificial nature.

Changes, changes, wherever one looked – even in Jim's diary. 'The clumsy rude boot...' reflected the growing influence of practice run answers to Eng. Lit. exam questions – and his growing practice of self-mockery, in itself a partial antidote to heartache, and indicative perhaps of increasing maturity. Besides, he had taken rather a fancy to some of Matthew Arnold's poems, because of their melancholy pessimism, "...this strange disease of modern life,/With its sick hurry, its divided aims"; and their deft touches of memories arousing beauty: "dark bluebells drench'd with dews of summer eves..."

*

"Ouch! Oh blast! Oh damn and blast!"

Nothing from Arnold there.

Jim sat on that springy turf vigorously rubbing his ankle. He had been kicking a ball about with Doug and Doug's younger brother, Terry and then – "turning round sharply at full speed." 'Ouch!' That left ankle had never been completely right (ho! ho!) since the Munich agreement had been signed.

The ankle swelled so badly that at home, Jim could only descend the crooked stairway on his "bottle and glass or arrière train" – far more poetic than plain 'backside'. Nothing else for it, but to rest the swollen ankle – no 'steady and forceful' contribution to the Bridge FC's performance that Saturday. "Cruel twist of fate and my ankle that I cannot play." Quite so, pun taken.

Once Jim could hobble without too much discomfort, he teamed up with Syd to visit their old school in Grove Lane, to find, not air raid shelters being built – but "brick walls outside certain classrooms as protection against blast." Shelters had been built in Handsworth Park.

Would they ever house 'fast Sue' and her pal Joan, who hadn't turned up for that bandstand date? What a young drip he had been in those far off days, he thought. Now he was fully prepared to live more dangerously. He headed for the boathouse and hired a skiff, for his maiden voyage in such a delicate, flimsy craft.

"Managed quite well, but you certainly have to be careful and sit tight."

His training on that black beast of a sofa at his Gran's was proving its worth yet again.

Jim the schoolboy also linked up again with friends whose insurance cards were now being stamped – the sophisticates of the modern industrial world. He found Ken staying at home "after having had the measles" – a recuperating pal who had become the proud owner of "a new super 'Sun' bike. Wish I had one like it." (Or even a second hand one – he still wasn't comfortable borrowing 'the trusty, or rusty steeds' of other boys.)

As in the distant past, these two friends attended a Guild lecture together, and Jim enjoyed the Saturday presentation of the Guild's Dramatic Society's *To Have and to Hold*. "Very good indeed for an amateur show. Only fault speeches did not flow easily enough. Ken as usual over-acted." Just as in the days of monkey running. However, Jim's overall assessment of his 'prone to showing off' friend was more charitable. "He seems to have settled down a great deal more. Good job too."

In the company of non-showing off friends Dave and Bob, Jim greatly enjoyed, for the second time, the comedy thriller, *The Cat and the Canary*, starring wise cracking Bob Hope and a delightfully dishy Paulette Goddard. On that day of hearty chortling, the ardent filmgoer made an abject confession – perhaps he had been distracted by pretty Paulette.

"Cor! Almost forgetting. Had a letter from Mary this morning. Very pleasant. Had an enjoyable holiday at Lynmouth. Not coming home till Dickie goes back. Shan't see her. D - - -, D - - -, as she says." Surely not dash, darn or drat? Must definitely be – Damn? Warmly encouraging especially from a convent influenced girl. But after all that Matthew Arnold stuff, wasn't "cor! Almost forgetting" really a woefully, and lamentably inelegant reaction? He applied his dad's dictum and ruled himself distinctly 'offside'.

He woke up and found himself seventeen years of age. A birthday card arrived from Mary, and, to Jim's surprise "also one from Dickie!" (Well, so far 'young brother' had given no clear cause to be scragged – and was probably grateful at being spared dire retribution.)

5th April, 1940 – not a patch on last year's birthday celebration of course, but in a scratch game of footer "ankle stood up well under strain. Elastic bandage is certainly a great help – and support." (A feeble pun but the temptation was all too clear.)

Just before returning to Stroud, depressing news came of the German invasion of Norway and Denmark, "retaliation to our sowing of minefields" (at sea). "Silly, shows it must have been planned months beforehand." Britain was attempting to prevent 'neutral' Norway from exporting iron ore to Germany. Germany had other ideas, to seize Norwegian ports and the iron ore and to establish bases from which to attack British shipping in the North Atlantic.

In Arnold's words, "...the turbid ebb and flow/Of human misery..." appeared well set to expand in almost every direction.

Chapter Fourteen
An End of Schooling

Back at Northfield, life was burgeoning like billy-oh, "daffodils out and buds shooting." Yet there was a minus side to jocund spring-to wit, or lack of same, a "seething, swarming mass" of fags running riot with their shrill, yelping voices and scruffy ways, a pernicious blight on the steadily greening up countryside.

'Grit your teeth lad,' muttered Jim to himself, 'you're seventeen now and the school sports are only two weeks away. Get some serious training in. You'll have Flash Rowlands to beat this year and the tall, long striding Dennis Higson,' who, in 1939, had won the Intermediate Championship so convincingly.

Up Folly Lane then, steady running through "woods, fields and farmyards" – with varying permutations of Dickie, Wilson and Brown. Around and around the pretty level Marling School fields, heavy going this after the April showers.

A shrewd move on Higson's part to enter the same three events as Jim – the long jump, the quarter and the mile. In a way, it was a bit flattering that Higson had made that choice for it suggested to Jim, that Dennis believed Norton to be his main rival for the championship. Time and times would tell – and distance, of course, for the long jump.

As for Jim's academic ambition to become a university student, this was suddenly blown to smithereens. It all had to do with his having chosen to study German instead of Latin. The Headmaster had now told him, in his final term, nota bene, that Jim might have to obtain a credit in Latin in four months "in order to go to university! Impossible. Feel mad that he couldn't have told me before."

Jim supposed that this insuperable hurdle had been placed in his way, because his main strength was English and that somehow, shortsighted, antediluvian clever clogs, behind ivy-clad walls, made a particular connection between English and Latin.

When he had calmed down a little, Jim asked himself what he actually knew of Latin – if there was any kind of base on which he could rapidly build. He soon realised that apart from a few Latin tags, he knew no more than what he had heard Ken, the great lover, sometimes chant, under his breath, before moving into bird snaring action. How did it go? Amo, amas, amatus, amant – or something like that. Not much to build on there. Oh, and there was something called the ablative, whatever that was.

Once his temperature had dropped a degree or two further, he grudgingly acknowledged that if, by some other means or route, he gained a university place, he would need to convince his dad that to go on studying would be the right thing to do. He saw no way of convincing the old Victorian donkey on that point.

And what about finances? To stand any sort of a realistic chance of gaining a scholarship, he would probably need another year at school. And how would that be financed?

Then again, at some stage he would be sure to join the services before undergraduate studies were completed.

Turning the problem over and over in his mind reduced the keenness of the disappointment he felt. And yet, and yet it would have been so much better to have been given a fair crack of the whip. Such maddening quirks of fate could so easily trip you up, elastic bandage or no, during one's youth. He smiled wryly.

The lack of £13 in the family coffers had given him the chance to study in Stroud. Now, he was to be denied the possible chance of a university place because he had not learned a dusty, dead language! Life could be really barmy at times. Did the 'Latins' have an appropriate tag to describe such a situation? The Germans did, or something near enough, 'Gegen die Dummheit kämpfen (or was it streben?) die Götter selbst vergebens.'

*

Having watched the Marling School Sports – "no music, no times given, no enthusiasm" – under a "leaden sky and incessant drizzle," it seemed only proper to evaluate such dismal proceedings as "an exceedingly poor show." Besides, the Senior quarter mile had been run in a dawdling sixty-seven seconds (according to Jim's watch). Pathetic!

No pixie for a mascot this year, no girlfriend to cheer him - but on the eve of the sports, Jim did receive an encouraging letter from Mary and with it, at long last, a photograph. "Not a very good one but it will do for the time being." The small black and white snap was mostly taken up by large rocks and boulders (not too symbolic of emotional shipwreck he hoped). On this defensive shore line, stood a smart looking young girl in skirt and jacket, a walking stick in gloved hands, looking out to sea and smiling enigmatically, dreamily, wistfully? Jim couldn't be sure - and he had no magnifying glass to help him decide. Mary might just have been thinking about dinner - she had a healthy appetite.

Whatever had prompted the smile, would the smile itself have vanished had Mary been able to read - "I have almost forgotten her among so much turmoil and bustle"? Plaguey fags seemed evermore numerous, and running up and down a partly and heavily rutted Folly Lane, required intense concentration if a dodgy ankle was not to be twisted again.

Sports Day arrived, chilly, grey and damp - no weather for achieving and maintaining warm, relaxed muscles. No bright blue sky, no bright golden sun like last year. April wasn't really the month for track and field. But evacuees couldn't be choosers. No, April for some sixth formers, seemed more the month for poets; good old, straight to the point Chaucer for one;

"When that Aprille with his shoures sote
The droghte of Marche hath perced to the rote"

And that new bloke, the English teachers kept praising - somebody Eliot. But what did he mean by "April is the cruellest month..."?

Somewhat disappointing on certain days, like the day of the heats and Sports Day itself - but "cruellest"? No, that was pitching things far too high.

By general agreement both the run-up and the jumping pit were "rotten." Dennis Higson "won as I expected", by 2", probably the difference between the two boys' respective leg lengths.

As in the glory year of 1939, Jim sped into the lead at the start of the 440 yards. But, despite the slight variations in pace he applied, he could not shake off that tenacious, long striding presence just behind his right shoulder. Higson timed his final spurt well and nipped past Jim in the final few strides. "57.2 Good time."

The championship was now virtually Higson's. But Jim was determined to make him puff hard to clinch it in the mile. At the longer distance, he was able to vary the pace more frequently and carefully held something in reserve for his final all-out sprint over the last sixty yards or so – but – "Higson just beat me in mile after a splendid race. Just pipped me on post after I had led all the way. Still I have nothing to complain about...glad Higson won championship...best runner in school, honestly speaking."

Like his dad, Jim was always ready to concede defeat graciously providing he felt he had been beaten – fair and square. And this time he had been.

Perhaps there was something to what Eliot had written after all, "April...mixing/Memory and desire."

Ah, the memories of last year and the desires of this.

*

High time now for serious revision – only a couple of months to the HSC exams, when a hot sun would be sure to be blazing down on hapless, sweating examinees.

'Some day,' thought Jim, 'some enlightened and imaginative educationalist might take the trouble to research the trials of wartime evacuees, swotting in conditions not conducive to swotting. Take distractions, chores and grub – just for a start.'

Even though his girlfriend was now some thirty to forty miles away, and shielded by convent type physical and moral walls, Jim found himself lured to other natural beauties, those so wonderfully and plentifully on show in the surrounding fresh, springtime countryside. Such enticing invitations to take a cycle ride or a walk "through woods in the mist. Delicate lacery of verdant young sprays entrancing."

Fearsome PT exercises and games also took up some time, even a "tripe game of cricket. A real story book village green pitch – daisies, dandelions and sheep excretion." Table tennis tournaments to arrange and play in, and later tennis on the Northfield court. And pitiless teachers still expected essays on 'Attack or Justify the

Epilogue in Shaw's *St Joan*'; and 'The Character of Hamlet as Seen in the Soliloquies' – to be handed in on time!

Between attempts to pen penetrating paragraphs on *The Scholar Gypsy*, time-consuming chores might need to be carried out, "Pumped in the evening. Tough work..." (periodically the water supply at Northfield had to be hand pumped). "Carried a lot of coke from stables to coke hole." Odd job gardening, including repairs to tennis net. And the inevitable 'your turn this evening' – washing and drying up – a sure fire way of separating the workers from the shirkers and of identifying the dodgers among the lodgers. One young squirt acquired a tolerated notoriety for always making "a dive for all the knives, forks, spoons, eggcups etc." and then spending "far too long on them."

A shrewd brain was held to lie behind the twinkling eyes and round shiny glasses of mouse like Maybury. Mouselike in appearance – with a pachyderm hide. Bombarded with jibes, jeers, sarcasm and sneers, he polished on, a bland, condescending smile on his face.

In some ways, boyish banter apart, such domestic chores arguably made for a state inferior to marriage – for when spliced, there could at least be some fun and frolics with the missis, as well as fatigues.

If the outputs of energy were varied and sometimes remarkably enjoyable, the inputs were mostly monotonous and near mountainous. Piles of bread and jam for breakfast, jam and bread for tea. And in between, canteen dinners of bits of gristly meat, cabbage and potato 'sog', followed by tombstone and custard (rhubarb pie). Treats were few but immensely enjoyed.

"Baggy and Mrs Baggy gave us" (the senior boys) "a decent supper in their room. What a luxury to taste a bit of cheese again" – a highlight diary entry. So was the arrival of a food parcel, "cake, jelly, carrots etc. Bless her. What a mother." The parcel was shared out in the dorm. It would be great to be home again for a few days – and to experience "the long expected thrill of tucking in to a real good meal." Get ready then.

"Hey Dickie, I'd like you to do me a favour."

"What's it worth?"

"Nothing if you do it. A thick ear if you don't."

"I'll tell my big sister of you."

"Good – she'll cuff your other ear."

"All right, what do you want me to do?"

"You know I want to go home for Whitsun and I can just about afford to, if I can travel half-price. That's where you come in."

"Oh, how?"

"Well, boys under sixteen can travel half-fare on the coach. So if I give you 4/6, you can buy the half-price ticket and then give it to me. Savvy?"

"Blow me, I never thought my sister would take up with such a swindler." Dickie chuckled. "But it's a good wheeze though. I'll do it. Let's have the 4/8 then, – which includes the agent's commission."

Jim took a mock swipe at Dickie's head but handed over the extra two pennies with a grin.

One further precaution was necessary.

"Shall have to have a good shave on Friday in order to diddle the bus company."

'In another place,' many MPs, and behind them much of the country, felt they too were being 'diddled' by their war leaders "...especially over our failures and gross miscarrying of our campaign in Norway. Chamberlain getting it 'in the neck'. Hope he gets kicked out of office. Stiff-necked, humbugging, obstinate old fool! Trying to win the war by means of an umbrella instead of rifle. We want the gloves off to fight a man like Hitler."

So much for Tuesday's thoughts.

On Friday not only were the gloves off, but knuckle-dusters were grimly on.

"Stap me! Momentous news this morning. Holland and Belgium have now been invaded by Nazis."

The so-called 'phoney war', when land forces had not been heavily engaged, was savagely, crushingly over. The Blitzkrieg had begun.

The Headmaster held a general rollcall at school and urged the coach trippers not to return home, or if they did, to return to Stroud on Saturday.

To a beardless 'man', the 'Northfieldites' opted for 'city risk' and home cooking rather than 'country safety' – and further dollops of tombstone and custard. "At last, the long expected thrill of tucking in to a real good meal. Grand, luscious, succulent."

With a wonderfully comforting sense of repletion, Jim now felt ready to tackle the evening paper.

"Hitler is following the Schlieffen Plan of 1914, an enveloping sweep on the right flank." Jim again recalled that *Illustrated* article and wondered if the unimpressive Low Countries' defences would hold against such armoured might.

He turned the pages of the newspaper and again found it interesting how, even during what appeared might be a major development, war news and commentary became muddled together with the everyday.

The paper showed a photo of three pleasant looking girls picking cowslips, and another of a 'Windmill Girl.' Openly misleading that – a land-girl (very warmly clad, on the ladder of a wind operated water pump). 'We could do with that sort of pump and maybe that sort of girl back at Northfield,' thought Jim.

"Ten years from now some athlete will run a mile in four minutes predicted Paavo Nurmi the 'Flying Finn'..."

"Seen that Pop?"

"What?"

"Nurmi reckons someone will run a four minute mile in ten years time."

"Rubbish. About as likely as man getting to the moon."

"Listen to this Mom! "Children and adults who eat in communal canteens will be healthier than they were before the war if caterers in these centres follow official advice on diets.""

"All my eye and Betty Martin. What do officials know about cooking except – make do with less. I'll bet they were never on the dole."

"'Ear, ear – we could do with you and more like you in our canteen Mom."

"I can well believe it. But turn the wireless on will you son – Webster Booth and Anne Ziegler will be singing soon. They'll keep John McCormack over there, quiet for a bit."

"Everyone expecting air raids here" in Brum. People, Jim included, sensed that hostilities, which so far had been at the periphery of their experience, would shortly and literally be brought closer and closer to home. But this Whitsun break ended cheerily enough – "went to Spaldings and bought my racquet. A last year's model which should have been 25/- but which he let me have for 15/-" (That racquet was to give excellent service for wildly erratic performances. The application of banana oil to the strings seemed to make no difference either way.)

*

Back at Northfield, as one of the many counter balances to revision swotting, a new card school was formed, consisting of the old 'hands' (ho! ho!) Syd and Alf – Des and Flash, the newcomers. Des, a fellow sixth former, had only recently transferred to Stroud, and Flash, he of sprinting fame, slicked back hair and military bearing, had moved into Jim's dorm. The best card sessions by far were held al fresco – in a field, in the warm May sunshine, after a bicycle ride, Painswick way. 'Would jackboots ever trample over that very English turf?' Jim wondered. The notion seemed obscenely absurd – and yet – yet only the wildly irresponsible would ignore the possibility. Jim shivered.

On the day Holland and Belgium surrendered (by-passing the Maginot Line hadn't taken long) Jim made another confession, the second within a few weeks. A full four days after the postman's delivery, he recorded receiving 'two very pleasant letters in one envelope from Mary.'

A full four days ... Crikey. That quotation from Byron he had pondered about in the long ago of last year, seemed to be increasingly valid.

"Man's love is of man's life a thing apart,
'Tis woman's whole existence."

May be so, but the important thing was that Mary had told him that he could "see her this Sunday at Tewkesbury."

And not only that, she had confirmed the date by a later postcard: 11.15 Sunday.

And not only that! Tewkesbury eh! That meant Mary was now prepared to meet him halfway between Worcester and Stroud, most encouraging pedalling wise – and, hopefully in other wise. Highly elated (but not with the 'pun') he went in search of Syd to request the loan of the trusty steed.

The Friday before *the* Sunday and pains in the neck, quite literally. Oh hell! hell! hell! "Baggy and Mrs B half afraid that I have got the mumps, but I am positive this is not the case...felt much better in the evening." Luckily, the headstrong Jim was right, the neck stiffness resulting from "fearful" PT exercises.

*

A warm sunny morning, a soft green countryside in its full fig of springtime glory. Such a difference from that drab, grey day when he had made his sortie from the pukka sahibs.

Jim arrived five minutes early, as chivalrous behaviour required, and Mary arrived on time.

"It's lovely to see you again Mary. Lucky with the weather aren't we?"

"You're looking well Jim – the Cotswold air and the Cotswold girls must suit you."

"Can't say about the girls, but I shall be sorry to leave Stroud."

They smiled at each other.

"Let's go to Twyning shall we. It's nice by the river there."

"Right ho, lead on MacLeigh."

So she did.

"Sat in field for hours, ate our dinner and lay and dreamed. Then rode to Tewkesbury and rowed on the Severn for an hour. Moored under the willows and had tea."

Dare he? Lounging in the stern seat in a bright, summery dress, her limbs lightly bronzed, the breeze gently ruffling her soft, wavy brown hair, Mary looked enchantingly pretty under the dancing light and shade of the willows. Dare he?

No, better not – the old signals of 'come kiss me sweet and twenty' still hadn't re-appeared. A force field of reserve, hers not his, held him in check. Anyway, a clumsy move of any kind across the boat and he might well find himself floundering in the Severn, maybe nudged on his way by Mary herself. Better to remain patient – and dry.

What was it the poet Browning had said? Ah, yes: "the first fine careless rapture." Was it only the song thrush who could recapture such wonderful feelings? If so, the thrush was indeed a lucky devil.

Odd and disturbing to think that not so very many miles from this quietly happy scene, a ferocious battle was being waged over the evacuation of some three hundred thousand British and Allied troops from the crowded, bloody beaches of Dunkirk.

But for Jim: "Most enjoyable day. As she grows older Mary improves which is saying a lot. These meetings after long periods of separation seem sweeter."

In earlier days, before his conversion from impressionable boy to impressionable youth, Jim would have written a letter to Mary within twenty-four hours of such "a really magnificent day". But what with swotting, "drawing up second round of table tennis competition", and concern about the war, "it certainly seems as though we have at last entered into a life and death struggle" he hadn't got round to writing. Mary had beaten him to it with "an extremely pleasant surprise, a very nice letter." Mary had experienced a puncture cycling home. Still, she would have coped all right with a cheery smile, and, hopefully, an un-convent like expression or two. What a girl!

Jim stared at the envelope, picked it up and let out a whistle of astonishment. Yes, it was plain enough – a distinct 'X' on the back of the envelope. "H'm I wonder! Feel very bucked. Wrote to her... and had a feed of radishes and bread and butter." Regrets about possible missed opportunities on the banks of the Avon, and later on the waters of the Severn might remain. But then, that was part of courtship. Better though to sing along with Henry Hall and his band;

"Here's to the next time
And our merry meeting..."

*

More welcome news from the home front -"that Dad has at last obtained a settled job. At a munitions factory, interrogating people as they enter the gates. Suit him down to the ground." Yes, the old Victorian would revel in his new found authority, but officiousness would be tempered with good-natured chaff, and, most assuredly, a pun or two. Some of the better dressed white collar workers might even be honoured with the occasional Byronic quote. Good old Pop.

Bad news again: "Italy has declared war on the Allies." Jim gave the thumbs up to the "stirring speech" made by the Minister of Information in Churchill's Coalition Government now in office for about a month. Duff-Cooper spoke of Italy as a country "famous for its ruins! Will be more so in the future." Hot dog!

At a bad and lonely time for Britain, optimistic and stirring words were not out of place. A curious atmosphere was developing – a mixture of not wanting to believe but still expecting that Britain would shortly stand alone: apprehension was palpable along with a fierce, yet at times amateurish resolve to resist a German invasion of Britain that daily seemed more imminent.

As the German troops neared Paris, Doug, Syd and Jim took a bus to Brum – "barricades all along roads. Stopped several times for Identity Cards." In England's "green and pleasant land", unsullied by invaders for centuries, the situation seemed unreal. Individual security checks were both disturbing and reassuring.

"Good to see Mom and Dad again, though Dad tired out by his job. Too much standing, coupled with heat and gammy leg. Curse this war!"

But healthy schoolboy spirits soon revived and after a grand "real breakfast of bacon and egg, and real marmalade. Magnificent," Jim joined Doug and Syd at the Arts Faculty building of Birmingham University for the oral exam in French. Pas du tout magnifique – still, it had been merveilleux to be chez nous again if only for un peu du temps.

Trouble not at t'mill but in t'dorm on Jim's return to Stroud. Jim was greeted with shrill, wailing complaints from the "smaller fry" protesting against the "ruthless" military discipline imposed by Flash, promoted to temporary boss during Jim's absence. Jim remained unmoved and warmly backed his deputy – "hope he larnt em."

Flash, a lad of about sixteen and a keen member of the school's Officers' Training Corps, was soon involved in training members of the LDV – the Local Defence Volunteers, (the Look, Duck and Vanish mob) later renamed the Home Guard. It seemed odd, and oddly British for a sixteen year old schoolboy to be teaching mature men (over ripe in some cases) the ways of war – or at least arms drill.

Unexpected things began to happen out of the blue – and partly expected things out of the black. One Sunday evening, Mary's parents, with Mary in tow, suddenly turned up at Northfield. Apparently, Dickie was being evacuated to Canada. And Mary? She too if her parents had their way. But "she is firmly resolved that she doesn't want to go." Not just resolved but firmly so, and by golly she could be firm.

And Jim's reaction? Shock. Little coherence in his whirling thoughts – and a churning, sickening feeling in his stomach. Of course, he wanted Mary to be safe – but at that distance? And why didn't she want to go? He couldn't prevent his heart from skipping a beat or two, but was careful not to flatter his hopes or himself too much. There could be many reasons for her reluctance to 'emigrate', so an honest "don't know what to think" completed the entry for the day.

*

With characteristic malice, Hitler sent his bombers on night raids in the Bristol area, to coincide with the start of the HSC final exams.

"At five minutes to one this morning air raid warnings sounded. Everyone bundled down to the garage and sat dithering in pyjamas on the cold floor. Most annoying." Late start for the "pretty foul" French exam. Next night – a similar occurrence. After just that first night's experience, "no panic...everyone looks on the raids as a matter of course now." Schoolboys soon become blasé. A third successive night of 'alarum' brought an improvement in the 'excursion' to "our new shelter in passage way. Much more cheerful. Light and able to play cards."

Adjusting to air raid alarms had not deflected Jim from thinking about the broad strategic outlook. "Russia up to her tricks again. Ultimatum to Rumania demanding concessions of Bessarabia. Seems as though she wants to prevent Germany from extending her influence to the Black Sea. Be a real world war soon."

Towards the end of June, Syd and Alf received news that really hurt. Their old comrade, of carefree cribbage evenings Pa Appleton, had died. Jim attended the funeral.

A day or two later, he reflected how incongruously a diary can quite unintentionally read. After a reference to that funeral (the first Jim had attended) Jim had written "Feel sorry for Mrs Appleton. Still lives at School House. Best arrangement as it will keep her mind occupied. Had terrific fights all aft. on the lawn. Poor Mrs Appleton."

One more heave and the exams would be over – and "in two weeks time I shall be an old boy."

During that fortnight, Jim behaved as though he had subconsciously decided to take every opportunity he could, to imprint on his visual memory, images of beauty from the Cotswold countryside – Painswick, Cranham and Haresfield Beacon for example. As he was still suffering from a hangover due to answering Eng. Lit. questions, his style remained somewhat self-conscious, slightly overblown. "Mist, distant hills, shafts of golden sunlight shooting down upon the ribbon of the Severn. The incessant silver arrows of rain." But the prosaic soon followed, as day follows diurnal. "Absolutely soaked when we got back. Had a meat pie."

As a valedictory literary effort, the gang of four card players compiled the 'Northfield Nark', with jokey illustrations by Flash. Written in an exercise book, this journal was hardly the biting satire it claimed to be. But the 'editorial staff' and the illustrator hooted, howled and hollered with laughter at their own facetious schoolboy humour. "Camping Hints: how to pitch a tent. Heat pitch until it melts then apply with a brush." Collapse of juvenile 'senior' schoolboys.

Time for lump in the throat adieux and au revoirs. Time for an emotional parting from Ma Appleton and teasing but tearful Pauline, after a "right royal tea". A warm handshake and an "excellent testimonial" from the Headmaster. Another good testimonial from Baggy. After a collection among the boys, presents for this genial master and his motherly, tubby wife. Handshakes with the 'Northfieldites' – even the smallest and scrawniest of fags. "It's going to be a big jolt to break away from all these affectionate ties." Some friends to be seen again, and some not. A bigger jolt still to leave the sheltered world of the schoolboy.

So homewards – but first a detour to Worcester. Jim was made welcome and treated kindly by Mary's aunt and uncle. But the aunt, it usually was the lady in such situations, posed the question that makes ex-schoolboys of a certain age squirm inwardly;

"So, what are you going to do now you have left school?"

A blank look. A slight pause.

"I don't know," the uncomfortable but expected response met with an understanding smile.

But what really mattered at the start of another spell in limbo, were the precious moments in Mary's company, chatting with her, and boating with her again on the Severn.

"Where do you think we'll be this time next year?"

"I wish I knew. Or perhaps I don't. Do you still want to be a nurse?"

"Yes, eventually, but Dad has ideas about buying a small farm."

"Oh, that's news. Whereabouts?"

"I'm not quite sure – but probably Belbroughton way."

"You're not going to Canada then?"

"No fear."

"Thank goodness for that."

Mary smiled.

"I suppose you'll soon be looking for a job?"

"Yes, but I wish I could have gone to university. Still it can't be helped. I might volunteer for the navy if Mom and Dad will let me."

"Well sailor, our time's nearly up – better start rowing back to the boat house."

*

And then, at the station – "leaning out of the carriage window to say goodbye, whistle went and our lips met as of mutual accord. All cares and anxieties melted away...returned my blown kiss, as train steamed out" to Brum.

Chapter Fifteen
Growing Up and Ducking Down

"Good luck son."

"Thanks Mom, I shall need it. But it's a pity the HSC results aren't out yet."

"It surely can't be long now before you hear something. But remember, don't just take any old job – try and find one where you think you'll be happy."

"Right ho."

"Got a clean handkerchief?"

"Yes Ma. Don't fuss."

Jim set off for yet another job interview, a job he could have taken as things turned out, at an estate agents, but at only five bob a week?! (Plus vague talk about possible commission). No bloomin' fear. A junior clerk with a firm of accountants then? Again no – that job "would have been all right two years ago when I had just obtained Matric." No point in undervaluing yourself.

Despite the fag of trying to find an appropriate job, Jim was pleased to be back home. His scorn for 'the dump' had gradually mellowed to slightly exasperated affection – the exasperation springing principally from the lack of a bathroom and a return to chamber-pot usage. But he rejoiced in the privacy of having a bedroom to himself again, free of fag pollution. His mother was just as fine a cook as ever, preparing the best of meals that rationing and income would allow. His dad, though so often weary from long hours of standing, was obviously bucked to be earning steady money, in itself a great tonic for self respect.

Yes, no doubt about it, although he missed the Cotswold countryside and bike rides, Jim was glad to be at home again. But it was a jolt, and no mistake, casting off the clouts of a schoolboy. True, he had been liberated from homework, tombstone and custard, and mounds of bread and jam. But, he did so miss the daily bouts of good-natured banter. Altogether, an unsettling business.

For the past twelve years, some 70% of his life, he had been a schoolboy. Even when confused and miserable, say with Algebra and Physics, such experience had been part and parcel of normal schooling. Other lads had struggled say, with French or Geography. The ups and downs, the proper 'umdrum, the triumphs and disasters all formed the natural elements of a schoolboy's life and times, a shared mixture of joy, depression and the commonplace. Now, it was all gone, and not yet replaced by any reassuringly familiar activity.

The world knew and acknowledged the schoolboy. The world knew and acknowledged the wage earner. Both conditions fitted in very readily to the general scheme of things. It was the passage from one state to the other that was so unsatisfactory, hit and miss, and messy. In such a martial age, it was a bit like unrhythmical marking time before falling into step again, to set off in a new direction, with a new focus and new colleagues.

In practical and less fanciful terms, intervals between sporadic forays into the job market were filled in a variety of ways – by games of tennis in Handsworth Park with reliable old Syd, hikes with Dave and with groups from church, boating with his nephew young Bill, a couple of enjoyable days at Aunt Millie's, table tennis, helping to decorate his bedroom – and solitary nostalgic walks around Cherry Orchard and Handsworth Wood. Instead of grass, corn now waved in those 'hey nonino' fields – fields of ripening corn overlooked by an aircraft spotters' observation post. Privacy gone – but not the memories. Oh boy! Oh boy! Oh boy!

Mary had written from "London at an hotel in Piccadilly, hobnobbing with admirals. Very slick. Hope she is having a good time." Jim wasn't bothered by the teasing reference to admirals, knowing that Mary's very protective dad would be nearby. But what had Mary's dad to do with admirals?

With a slight sense of shock, Jim, as a would be wage earner, realised how little he knew about what Mary's dad actually did for a living. He just knew him to be an engineer of some sort. Could be something hush hush, he supposed.

Well, no need to be hush hush about the daily tally of German aircraft being shot down over Britain. The diary recorded sixty, fifty, sixty-six, sixty-two, seventy-eight – punishing losses and no mistake.

Then on 14th August, having just replied to Mary's admiralty slanted letter Jim heard:

"...one or two thuds: at about quarter past eleven the sirens broke upon the stillness of the night with their discordant wailing. We were down in Ridgeways' shelter until five past three. Several lulls in the action. Our guns firing, shrapnel falling, bombs dropping, highly exhilarating though boring during spells of inactivity."

Such was one personal and private account of Birmingham's first 'real' air raid. Fear was not mentioned but that must have been present, if largely masked, partly by excitement at coming under fire for the first time, partly by masculine pride when a lad is sharing a shelter with a neighbour's daughter, a charmer who bears a startling resemblance to glossy, raven-haired Dorothy Lamour!

And at seventeen, Jim no doubt still wore the invisible flak jacket of youth believing itself to be miraculously bomb and bullet proof, a belief which proved such a potent ally for recruiters, especially those of a totalitarian conviction.

Damage was inflicted by the raid "to Nuffields, Hook and Eye and several houses." As for casualties, Jim wasn't sure. Numbers meant little because, understandably, he had almost no conception of the agonising atrocities that could be done to human bodies by searing chunks of jagged metal ripping into flesh and bone. The only dead person he had ever seen was Uncle Frank, simply looking sound asleep in his front room, a slight smile formed by his lips – Dad's brother who had been badly gassed during World War I. And now it was World War II with its death and destruction from the air.

Various other raids were launched on Brum before the 'big one' of 25/26th August. These gave Jim a clearer idea of the possible reasons why his dad had refused to go into an Anderson air raid shelter, choosing to remain in bed, and adopting a common fatalism – 'if your number's on it (the bullet or the bomb) there's nothing you can do about it.' But Jim recognised that for his Dad to take shelter in the corrugated steel hutch, in next door's back garden, he would need to be lifted in and out, almost like a stiffened corpse because of his gammy leg – a burdensome, possibly painful and certainly demeaning procedure. 'Not worth the candle'.

On 18th August, with the Battle of Britain at its height, Jim learned, from the newspaper, that he and his pals had passed their HSC exams. "Hoorah. Very pleased."

Another raid, and then, on that same morning, just after breakfast, Jim heard the latch of the garden gate click.

"Mom, It's Uncle Les – come to see if we're all all right, I'll bet."

Jim went into the garden to greet his cribbage mentor uncle.

"Nice new bike you've got there, Uncle Les."

"Think so?"

"Sure so. It looks a real snip."

Uncle Les grinned his broadest of Fred Astaire grins.

"Yes, it is, isn't it. And," he paused for effect, "it's all yours Junior."

"What?!"

"You heard, it's yours – or put another way, it's for you."

"For me?! But why? Why on earth ...?"

Jim began to splutter.

"Oh do close your mouth. You remind me of a codfish on a fishmonger's slab. I just thought it was about time that the brains of the family had a bike – and now you've got your HSC and are looking for a job, well..."

"B...b...but...how can I ever repay you?"

"Don't be a twerp. It's a present. After all, you did beat me at crib – once. Just be sure to look after it. It's not new."

But what a bike – Jim's own, his very own, a BSA "...trigger control three speed. Oil bath...runs very easily and smoothly. Syd called and we went a ride. One hundred and forty-four Nazi planes down."

Several nights of peace – shelter free. Jim, still job hunting and striving to come to terms with lunacy, "...helped Mom with the housework and then went for a ride round Sutton. The park looks lovely with its great sweeps of purple heather and one wonders why the world and its occupants should so suddenly become mad when there are so many beautiful things to behold in life."

Madness returned – seven hours in the shelters during 24th/25th August and seven hours ten minutes the following night. (Methodical Germans – still quantity counting Jim.) A great advantage now – having outside lavatories.

"Market Hall has been burned to ground, only skeleton remaining. Delayed action bombs in Perry Barr, back of Odeon. Great number of incendiary bombs dropped. Round by Dave's, Bill's, Cherry

Orchard Road – glad Mary isn't here – Kynochs. Parts of Perry Barr roped off. Wrote letters after jobs. 10 to 10 again to night Jerry came over." (Yes, very methodical.)

In the same entry, reference was made, twice, to "most uncanny queer swishing sounds" – some of the many incendiary bombs showering down locally. Jim dozily remembered his fag cards and sleepily wondered if the twin set ladies were doing their stuff with metal scoops and buckets of sand.

Next morning Jim, at his dad's request, and with a mixture of excitement and apprehension, wheeled out his new bike and rode to Alec's in Erdington: "...had to make many detours due to unexploded bombs and burst gas and water mains." Everything OK at Court Lane. Alec, on leave "looks very well and tanned." So, on to May's. OK there too but "a lot of incendiaries down their road." Back to base, mission complete. Even better than OK at base, for a letter from Mary had arrived; "signed tout mon amour. That's the spirit."

Rather a lukewarm reaction to an ardent signing off? What, no 'je suis aux anges' this time? Why the unromantic reaction? There was no other girl in Jim's life at this stage. And "tout mon amour" into the bargain! An avowal of love, even if it was in French (out of modesty, mock or real) would have sent him into raptures in the past. What was wrong? Perhaps lack of sleep, perhaps 'aux anges' was tempting fortune too much when bombs and shrapnel were hurtling from the ciel.

But faithfully, he wrote back the next evening. After a light-hearted and low scoring game of billiards with Dave at the Congregational Church's Social Centre, "continued Mary's letter in shelter during the customary air raid." And next day he bought a birthday present for Mary, "a bottle of 'June' perfume. I remember the fragrance from last Christmas." Indeed he did.

Yes, he still cared and cared deeply. But because of the separating distance and far 'quieter' nature of Mary's world, her circumstances seemed so very different from his own. He clung to the memory of that fragrance of Christmas past. He took a deep breath – and gave a feeble imitation of a Bisto kid.

Just the right romantic curtain raiser for a visit to the 'soldiering on' Theatre Royal up town, with Dave and his mom to see, but more particularly to listen to Richard Tauber in *Land of Smiles*. His singing "excellent" but "plot and acting very mediocre."

Sporadic air raids on Birmingham continued but not with the same ferocity as on 25/26th August. Parts of Perry Barr remained cordoned off because of unexploded bombs (UXBs), with policemen nearby on security duty. "Dad's place has been hit but not so severely." London continued coping with the Blitz.

Then on 9th September a whole new rhythm to Jim's life began. His 'marking time' period was over. He had become a wage earner. Hours 8.30 – 12.30: 1.15 – 5.15, alternate Saturday mornings off. Wage 26/- a week. "Not too bad at all." Employer – Henry Hope & Sons Ltd., Smethwick – manufacturers of metal window frames and metal doors, located not far from The Hawthorns, home of the Baggies.

Having been near the top of a schoolboy's ladder, Jim stepped across to a white collar employment ladder – with who knew how many rungs above him? Of course, one or two rungs were already 'beneath' him – 'him with his HSC' – the post boy's job for instance, and that of the office boy.

Having been taken on as a junior clerk in the Accounts Dept., Jim was almost immediately assigned to war work. Day two "printed and stuck labels on boxes for Spitfire Fund"; Day three "ruled off pages and entered details for Air Raid Casualty Book." He crossed his fingers, hoping his own name wouldn't appear in that particular register.

From a world where, as a senior schoolboy, Jim had felt comfortably and confidently at home, he had suddenly moved into a world essentially peopled by adults. Adults were nothing new, of course, as parents, relatives, neighbours, teachers but now, in an office, everyone, until the arrival of a downy chinned office boy, was his senior and some among them mighty bosses. These important people, at expansive desks in individual offices had clear expectations of punctuality, workloads, performance and behaviour to be satisfied. No private study periods now and 'larking about' sessions, schoolboy style, were fini, replaced by the disciplines and routines of paid employment.

But he was pleased and encouraged to note that 'larking about', office romance intrigue style, flourished readily enough.

Friday, 13th September. Appropriately a day of mixed fortunes but with an additional, troublesome ingredient – a looming, soul searching dilemma.

"Received my first wages. Can honestly say that it gave me very little thrill although Mom was delighted as a child." Understandable of course, given the sacrifices made over the years to ensure her only chick received a good education. Sal felt fully entitled to treat herself that evening to a milk stout – and with a satisfied air of 'I told you so' she treated her husband to an extra half pint of ale.

But the wage earner himself (or was he a salaried employee he wondered) had a troubled mind. The three speed gear on his bike had gone wonky, making it difficult to cycle up the steep part of Island Road to work. His conscience and his emotions also seemed, much like his gears, in a wonky condition. "Wish I could see Mary and confide in her. Need someone. Am tempted by Julie but know deep down that no one can ever replace Mary. At least that is how I feel at the early age of seventeen."

Surely to goodness he was not referring to Jittery Julie, the 'nervous breakdown' girl with whom he had once taken a walk on the wild side through a churchyard? No, this Julie was a slender, willowy girl with pleasant features, dark hair combed into an attractive page boy bob. A girl with a quiet but friendly disposition. But remember the old saying, muttered the wage earner to himself, 'Still waters run deep'.

Julie formed one of the party of six young (Social Centre) ramblers who after that Friday pay day, and a Saturday morning's work, tramped around the Lickey Hills. Four lissom lassies escorted by Dave and Jim. No problem with the gender imbalance for there were no pairings and no wallflowers among the gang. No billings no cooings. Just, "Most amusing backchat, leg pulling and the like. Friendly chaffing, the spirit of English youth is still alive and will flourish undaunted despite horrors of war and Nazi atrocity."

Shortly after setting off for home, from the Lickey terminus, the sirens began to wail presenting an all too common transport problem. Stay put – like the tram, and wait for the all clear – or take a chance and start walking in the hope that the air raid 'proper' would not materialise, or if it did, be a short one.

"Well, you flowers of chivalry, what do you think we should do?"

The question was put to Dave and Jim by jolly, round faced and bouncy Hilda.

"Stap me, and I've gone and left my armour, shield and lance at home," said Jim.

"And my cuirass is at the cleaners."

"Your what Dave?"

"You heard."

"Stop fooling about – what do you really think we should do, you two?"

Evelyn frowned slightly as she looked with attempted schoolmarm severity at the two lads.

"Well, we are taking a chance either way but I think we'll do better by walking."

"I agree," said Dave.

(What Jim hadn't said was that he didn't want his mom to become increasingly anxious and cross by turns if he was late home for his 'bit of supper'.)

"What do you think girls, shall we trust them?"

Hilda looked at the other three girls.

"Only as far as the outer circle."

It was Hilda's pal who had answered – Ellen, a fair-haired girl with the dry wit of her Scottish parents.

"Right, that's settled then. Best blistered feet forward."

The tiring but cheery party of six began the long steady climb towards Northfield.

"Come on Jim, let's hear 'Poor but Honest' from you."

"If you insist."

"We do, we do," chanted the girls – but not Dave. Dave had a good, strong voice but didn't know the words of the 'tear jerker'.

"But I don't know all the verses," said Jim.

"Just as well."

"And what do you mean by that Miss Saucebox?" Jim looked with mock sternness at Ellen.

"Simply that I wouldn't want you to overstrain your vocal chords. Still I've got a few Zubes left."

"Oh stop it you two – get on with it Jim."

So he did.

""She was poor, but she was honest,
Victim of the squire's whim:
First he loved her, then he left her,
And she lost her honest name.

Then she ran away to London,
For to hide her grief and shame;
There she met another squire,
And she lost her name again.

In the rich man's arms she flutters,
Like a bird with a broken wing:
First he loved her, then he left her,
And she hasn't got a ring.

See him in the House of Commons,
Making laws to put down crime,
While the victim of his passions,
Trails her way through mud and slime.

Standing on the bridge at midnight,
She says; 'Farewell blighted Love,'
There's a scream, a splash – Good Heavens!
What is she a' doing of?

Then they drag her from the river,
Water from her clothes they wrang,
For they thought that she was drownded;
But the corpse got up and sang:""

"Come on, all together now."

""It's the same the whole world over;
It's the poor what gets the blame,
It's the rich what gets the pleasure,
Ain't it all a blooming shame?""

"It'll be a right bloomin' shame if we miss that bus. Come on you lot."

Hilda made a tired, heavy footed sprint for the Number 11, outer circle bus as it pulled into Selly Oak. The other five ramblers followed close behind. Sobs and sighs of relief – and broad grins as they flopped on to worn, shabby seats that now seemed luxuriously soft. The bus set off to thread its way through Harborne, Winson Green –

past the grim looking prison, Perry Barr and on to Erdington where Julie and Evelyn lived.

In retrospect, a great ramble but, as so often, came the reckoning.

"NB. Last night on bus held Julie's hand. God knows what for. Felt today as though I had betrayed a great trust – O Hell."

Was the hand holding a form of mutual reassurance during an air raid threat? Was it in any way amorous in intent? Crikey, did it matter? Did it? In these 'green and salad' days, Jim endured not continuous but periodic spasms of acute internal soul searching– a bit like emotional colic really.

And all this emotional turmoil less than two months after that poignant kiss as the "train steamed out". One more example of that age old tussle in man's history – a tussle that became particularly acute in wartime – the battle of Separation vs. Propinquity. Propinquity? Such a pompous word. A dance band tune lyricist had a better word for it;

"It's not the pale moon that excites me,
That thrills and delights me,
Oh no, it's just the nearness of you."

With his emotions all at sea, Jim wondered whether he would be better off afloat in the navy, far removed from deeply unbalancing damsel delight. He wrote away for details and an application form for an officer cadetship.

On that Sunday of emotional anguish, one hundred and eighty-five German planes had been shot down in defending Britain– a record – prompting Jim to repeat in his diary, Churchill's earlier stirring tribute to the Battle of Britain airmen; "Never in the field of human conflict was so much owed by so many to so few."

*

Gradually, a steady but jagged pattern developed in Jim's life divided as it was between home, work and play. Each segment of the pattern could be and often was interrupted by "perishin' air raids".

Air raid warnings at work he didn't mind too much, staying "in our bolt holes being a pleasant relief from work …" Not that the work was particularly arduous, or tedious for that matter – at least in the learning stages of keeping ledgers straight and up to date. He quite enjoyed using the cylinder dictaphone, and obtained great satisfaction from bashing away at the heavy, cumbersome adding machine. A forceful pull on the handle, against spring tension, was required to record each keyed in set of figures, quite helpful for strengthening the wristiness of his table tennis strokes.

Air raid warnings at home, during the hours of darkness, were only to be expected as a natural part of modern warfare. Loss of sleep often meant a 'like a wet rag' condition at work but back home again, there might be *Crime Wave at Blandings* to listen to on the radio – a great pick me up.

Conditions in the air raid shelter were cramped, stuffy, smelling slightly but not objectionably so, of damp earth and anxious humanity. But Pat, the Dorothy Lamour beauty from next door, a year or two older than Jim, with her cheery infectious giggle, helped to lighten and brighten the atmosphere no end. Dear Pat, not for Jim, but a winsomely cuddlesome girl if ever there was one. In 'going round the back' to 37 (the front door was seldom used during the blackout) via the tunnel like entry, Jim often had to push his way past 'Dorothy' and the admirer of the month. A rippling, trilling girlish giggle would float after him all the way to his back door.

So, air raid warnings while at home or at work became an acceptable, if unwelcome, fact of wartime life for Jim. What did get his goat were air raid warnings wailing away when he was at play – usually in the Social Centre at church. The Centre was rapidly becoming the main focus of Jim's leisure interests when 'free youth' as distinct from 'wage slave'.

This fine church hall had been erected to the memory of those church members who had lost their lives during the Great War. It contained two full sized billiard tables, flanked by raised upholstered benches for spectators and players in waiting; space for two table tennis tables, a stage, radiogram, piano, tea bar and 'cloaks.' With table tennis tables packed out of the way, and French chalk liberally strewn over the floor – the Saturday night hop could get under its swinging radiogram way to Joe Loss, Geraldo, Ambrose – to 'In the mood' and 'Begin the Beguine'. Hot dog!

With an unsettling mixture of envy and admiration, Jim would watch the 'lady killers' stride confidently across the floor smirking smugly in their knowledge that they were sure to succeed. Rarely indeed, did they suffer rebuff. The chosen ones, always pretty, demurely or forwardly smiling, needed no persuasion, no entreaty, to waltz, quickstep or fox-trot with such dashing fellows, such triflers, such bounders.

Jim wondered whether he wanted to be a bounder. Could he be? Practice as he might, he knew he would never master the intricate dance steps, the little flattering attentions and turns of phrase that girls seemed to enjoy so much, and blush at occasionally. If he couldn't pay an honest compliment, he'd rather keep quiet. So, many of his clumsy dancing attempts remained mostly silent affairs, punctuated by 'oh sorry' as yet again he kicked a trim ankle, or trod on the toes of a neatly sandalled foot.

Then again, his physique and appearance were not up to snuff as gigolo material. He was not tall, good looking or stylishly dressed. He wasn't blessed with glossy black hair. If he attempted to grow a raffish toothbrush moustache, he knew it would not turn out to be of silky sable hue but an unprepossessing sandy ginger like his grandad's.

No, he would have to settle for the quieter, less pretty, hopefully still-waters-run-deep type of dancing partner.

Despite air raids, the enticements of games and of damsel delight at the Social Centre, Jim stayed in touch, if less and less frequently, with old school pals, with Doug – and more often with Syd. Syd and Alf, on one of their jaunts rode to Romsley Hill and left a message of good cheer to be passed on to Dandy Sandy, now in a sanatorium, a fact difficult to grasp. Such an ebullient spirit – to be laid low with consumption. Life could be cruel. Since the war had hotted up, so had the destruction of some of the old, reassuring certainties, physical and moral. The historic Market Hall was now a burnt out shell – and just how did one come to terms with some of the horrors of 'man's inhumanity to man'?

"Item of Nazi barbarity...British liner conveying evacuees to Canada reported torpedoed six hundred miles out in Atlantic. Seventy-nine out of ninety Government sponsored lost."

Jim felt sick as he realised that but for a change of mind by their parents, Mary and Dickie could well have been on that ill-fated ship. He struggled, as he often did, after an initial highly emotional reaction, to bring his thoughts to a better and calmer balance.

"Still it must be remembered that Nazi commander most probably was ignorant of the identity and nature of ship's cargo. Not that I am attempting to justify this action but am really attempting to take an impartial view and not work myself up into a passionate frenzy of hate as the newspapers would have us do. Spoon fed with propaganda."

He had recalled that he had read somewhere that the first casualty of war was truth – on both sides of the conflict.

The war ground on. De Gaulle landed with a Free French force in Dakar, Africa. The George Cross – the civilians' VC was instituted. The butter ration was reduced to 2 oz. The RAF bombed Berlin, the Fokker works in Holland – and the Krupp works at Essen – "ought to raze that dump to ground. Nazi planes wreck St Paul's high altar" – what a symbolic contrast.

After taking her home, after one particular all clear, 'playboy' Jim held Julie's hand again. "Oh hell, my thoughts are in a tumult but I am determined now to live only for the present and enjoy myself as much as possible – within reasonable limits." A total commitment to hedonism ran completely against the essential grain of Jim's character!

As if by way of reproach for the hand holding, on his mother's birthday (14th October) Jim received "an affectionate letter" from Mary. "Wishes me best of luck in navy exam and makes cracks about a girl in every port. Sends me fondest and all her love. Oh boy! Oh boy! Oh boy! Motherly advice about air raids."

Jim needed it. But maidenly comfort, of a physical nature would have been better, so much better. War was indeed, hell!

Chapter Sixteen

Whizz! Whizz! Whizz! And Gee Whizz!

Straight after his mom's birthday – what a pasting!

15th October, 1940 "Had just got going in the social when sirens went. Bombs were dropping and guns firing so we trooped into the shelter. Fun and games," (pass the parcel etc.) "Air raids certainly have one good effect, they bring out the best in people. Went out occasionally to see what was about...red glow in the sky from a fire somewhere town way. Went home about one and went to bed during a lull. Had been in bed about an hour when whizz! whizz! whizz! three bombs came whistling down. Instinctively threw clothes in front of my face in case of flying glass but fortunately did not explode. Wardens came looking in our garden to see if they could see unexploded bombs. One fifty yards away, corner of road by telephone box. Burst main. Immediately roped off and many people evacuated. Hope we don't have to go. Sobbing women and children, wrapped in blankets hurrying off into the night. Felt horribly tired at work."

But that wasn't the end of the 'excitement' for the day. No siree! After a sluggish day at work,

"Dashed home. Hurried off to Alex, (city centre theatre) a rattlin' good performance of *Ghost Train*. Few people there. Just leaving, sirens blowing, near exit, two shattering detonations, blast blew doors open. Dashed back into theatre. Entertained – quite jolly. Early all clear. Tram home." (exciting – very... Style, courtesy of Mr Alfred Jingle, of *Pickwick Papers* fame.)

With the ghost train 'derailed', cast and audience had together devised an impromptu concert in which the jaunty, bomber defiant singing of 'The Donkey Serenade' featured with gusto.

During these autumn weeks of mayhem, when Birmingham and other industrial cities of the Midlands experienced their 'blitz', Jim learned of the Admiralty's snooping. Was he sober? The notoriously abstemious sea lords wished to know – a question directed to the church minister. As various naval bulletins reached him, Jim, with a sickening feeling of disappointment, increasingly realised that his hopes of a cadetship had been founded on naive romantic rather than hard headed, realistic notions. Miserably, he acknowledged, to himself, that he was out of his depth – possibly academically, probably socially and certainly financially.

Was he "being helped by an army tutor for forthcoming exam?" What a daft question! "Not arf," was his sardonic diary reply. Despite the social polish applied at Stafford House by the Cap and Memsahib, Jim believed he would still find himself self-consciously struggling among the public school mores, and complex cutlery of a ward-room, and, worst of all, "large sums of money are required for uniform, mess bills etc." In short, cadetship notion – kaput, or rather, because there was a war on – kaputt.

So he wrote to the Air Ministry – and hoped.

*

"Five perishin' raids at work. Up and down, up and down but after two alarms it was decided we should continue working. Better really, although a little risky as we are in the top storey and there is piles of glass about" – the office block being quite modern with plenty of large windows, as befitted a metal window frame manufacturer.

And next evening – similar interruptions, different location – the Social Centre again and keenly contested table tennis "until the sirens went. We all stood at the door watching the shells burst over Coventry way. Pleasant with Julie but I wish Mary were here. Dave and I took Ellen home. Had hardly left her at her doorstep when the guns opened fire. Dived into an entry."

"Well Dave, how many entries have you dived into so far this month?"

Dave let rip with a characteristic, deep guffaw before answering.

"I can't see that it's any of your business, but if you must know," Dave broke off to make a quick count in silence, "about ten I should think, counting this one."

"How many times with Hilda?"

"None of your ruddy business."

Flashes of pale light flickered at irregular intervals at either end of the entry, where semi-circles of sky remained visible. Between sharp bursts of ack ack fire, the drone of distant planes could be heard. Occasionally, a much brighter flash would briefly light up this make shift shelter, followed by a low but deepening rumble – probably falling bricks and masonry thought Jim. Like stiff, probing fingers, rays of light slowly arced, back and forth, across the night sky.

"She's a bit of a bright spark isn't she?"

"Who is?"

"Hilda."

"She sure is," Dave chuckled.

"I was just thinking…"

"Wonders will never cease."

"…how Irene might be getting on these days."

"Oh, you mean Mary's old pal?"

"That's right."

"Oh, I expect she's OK Gosh, what a lot of water has gone under the bridge since those days. Weren't we a couple of young twerps?"

"Speak for yourself."

"Have you any plans for seeing Mary?"

"Not at the moment."

The conversation stopped briefly – then,

"Ellen's a nice girl isn't she?"

"Yes."

"And Julie?"

"Yes."

"And Pat – your neighbourly Dot Lamour?"

"Yes."

"A girl in every entry, eh Jim. You'd be a natural in the navy."

Jim winced – but Dave couldn't see that.

"Come on, it's a bit quieter now. I think we can make a dash for it."

The friends ran together towards the Odeon – still out of commission because of the UXB lying somewhere among its foundations. Near that majestic palace, they separated and made for their respective homes.

*

The autumn dating – girl friend courting game was certainly becoming complicated. Jim took stock of the situation.

Mary he knew well and cared for deeply – but she seemed so far away, virtually inaccessible what with the winter blackout and the bombing raids. Julie he was growing to like more and more, and now Ellen, a new friend, was really jolly good company, highly accomplished at badinage, if not much cop at table tennis. Since that 'poor but honest' Lickeys ramble, Dave had ardently begun pursuing Hilda, that bubbly, bespectacled girl whose bosom pal was Ellen. So Dave's close friend, Jim, began to see another foursome developing (as in the days of Ken) a natural enough process but fraught with potential soul searching complications given Jim's yearning to see Mary again, the steady pull of the quiet charm of, ready to hold hands Julie – and the fact that girls, once they were eighteen, like Ellen and Hilda, seemed to grow all misty eyed when they began chatting about wartime weddings. Crikey! Box clever Jim lad, like legendary Jimmy Wilde.

Perhaps this fizzing inner turmoil and lack of sleep due to air raids, which had turned "station, C & A, Marshall & Snelgroves, Boots, Hippodrome into burned shells of buildings" were partly to blame for what happened. Anyway, the essential facts appeared in the accident report.

"Stap me! Knocked an old chap down this morning. His own perishin' fault. He was crossing road, looking neither to left nor right, when he suddenly stepped back right into my path. Both went down. He was OK I think. Put him on his feet, straightened handlebars and pedalled off."

"Put it out of your thoughts," said Jim. "It's Saturday tomorrow and you're going with Dave to the pictures. Just think though, only two years ago, on a similar Saturday he, Jim that is, not Dave, had been enjoying a super duper time with Mary at the Witton fairground. Was this part of what Shakespeare might have meant by his 'whirligig of time and its revenges'? Still, try and look on the bright side." Jim readily acknowledged that *Pinocchio* was "a wonderful production. Makes you realise that after all there is something beautiful and creative in the world."

Emerging into the darkness, destruction yet once more. The friends saw a "huge glowing fire, engines tearing to town. Bombs quite close again. Stap me."

On that same beauty and brutality Saturday evening a "large number of casualties in a shelter by the Villa Cross. Thank God, Mary and I were not there."

A few days later people were killed on one of the old monkey run trails, Birchfield Road. Jim's old, friendly, ordered world was steadily being destroyed, and he wondered how he might react if he came across a badly wounded person or a shattered corpse. Again he thought of gentle Uncle Frank, the badge of the wounded ex-serviceman in his jacket lapel. He had looked so blissfully peaceful before burial. Dignity attached itself to a coffin but not to a pile of brick rubble.

Yes, air raid casualties would be a very different matter. Jim supposed that faced with a shattered limb, blood gushing from a gaping chest wound, he would first retch violently, vomit probably, and then, he hoped, try to do something useful under the guidance and supervision of an experienced person.

Better not become too introspective. Hop it to your spooky castle, Hamlet old sport.

"Oh, I'm glad to see you're back with us again. What have you been day dreaming about this time?"

"Oh this and that."

"Your face looked grim, for a youngster. Come on, you can tell your mother surely."

"Well, I was thinking of *Pinocchio* and then Uncle Frank and..." He saw his mom frown. Jim had a flash of inspiration. He grinned "...and 'Skipper' sardines."

"Skipper sardines! Whatever possessed you to..." Sal laughed. "I've got it. You young blighter – or bloater – you've been peeping haven't you?"

"Not really. I could hardly miss them 'cause your knitting didn't exactly cover them. And it was you who sent me to grammar school so that I could put two and two together."

"Here you are then, you artful monkey."

Sal handed to her son a set of bright yellow oilskins-cape, leggings and sou'wester. This really spiffing "A1, cycling outfit" although a present from his mom, had probably been paid for, partly, out of his own earnings. He had been handing over his weekly pay packet, without a second thought, to his mother. Recently he had received a pay increase, an encouraging surprise – a rise he didn't query. It wasn't his birthday but perhaps he had completed a probationary period satisfactorily. Anyway, he was now on 29 bob a week – 27/5 clear, "not bad at all."

Now that he was getting to know them better, wage earning Jim enjoyed the company of his colleagues. Tony, always in high spirits, a full of fun practical joker: Martin, young, tall, handsome, fair-haired and married, who took a closer interest than seemed really necessary for office routine purposes, in a plump, sweet-faced, redheaded girl in the adjacent office.

Jim tended to chum up with Arthur, a married man with two young children. Sometimes, on mild days, these office mates munched their lunchtime sandwiches together, sitting on the nearby railway embankment. On a Saturday in late November they formed a left wing partnership, playing for Hopes against Dudley Co-op Sports – a win for Hopes 2 – 1 – "fast and furious game. World of difference between this and school football." 'Steady and forceful' held himself to be "not exactly an outstanding success" – as a total beginner at outside left. He derived some consolation from the fact that he had been the youngest member of the team.

Some of the older male clerks, say aged forty and upwards, seemed abysmally middle aged, serious minded, grizzled and sometimes downright liverish. Poor Paul though, couldn't help turning from grey to sallow yellow on occasion, for he had contracted malaria while serving with the RAF in India. But old 'Dodgers' was quite a different case. 'Dodgers' "is swinging the lead again. Has been absent today and his holidays start on Thursday. What an old swindler he is." (Some colleague had tartly remarked, 'He has more time off than a prostitute's knickers!') A stab of conscience – balance the ledger properly lad – "all the same he is quite a decent old bird."

As for authentic birds, those in the office were quite presentable but mostly of an age when they were keen for a change of status from single to married and so rather patronising, supercilious even, towards a young goof with a twisted tooth – Higher School Cert. or no.

All except Miss Iris Bendall. Jim couldn't quite make up his mind about Miss Bendall. He knew well enough, on most occasions anyway, when she was teasing him, and felt rather flattered by such interest, which didn't fall neatly into the 'older sister' category of leg pulling. But he did sometimes wonder what Miss Bendall's motives might be.

Miss Bendall was a slim, trim brunette who wore dark rimmed glasses. She had pleasant features, a ready smile and a readier wit. But she must have been at least twenty-two, twenty-three even – and unattached, so Jim had been told.

"'Fraid I had to disillusion Miss Bendall. She actually thought I was twenty…sure she was disappointed. Asked me if my girlfriend had knitted my gloves (Some hopes) Telephone calls – 'from your girlfriend, I suppose?'" asked Miss Bendall with becoming archness.

Jim wondered, more than once, if his life might have become a great deal more interesting if he had lied about his age – adding on say just two or three years.

A youthful youth or no, perhaps it was high time he became a little more sophisticated so, during one of the quiet, siren free evenings at home, he started to "read some of Pamela Frankau's short stories. Extremely weird and very complex. Most difficult to see what she is driving at. Don't suppose she knows herself. These complex, involved and obscure writers seldom do."

Jim broke off from writing this penetrating critique and glanced across at his Mother.

"Don't you ever get tired of knitting Mom?"

"Sometimes."

"Have you ever knitted anything for Cecil?"

"Who the dickens is Cecil?"

"Come on now – you must remember, the chap in the song."

"Remind me."

""I'm knitting a singlet for Cecil

A nice woolly singlet for Cecil…

Oh, he might get a chill both behind and before,

I think I will add on a few inches more…""

"Hush up a minute, cheeky Charlie. I thought I heard the garden gate go. Yes, someone's coming up the yard. I wonder who it can be."

They soon knew.

"Hello Nan. How do Pop. Good evening old grammar bug."

It was breezy Bill, grinning broadly as he shook the fine drops of mucky November mist from his glistening raincoat – and warmed his hands at the open fire.

"Take the weight off your feet. Cup of tea?"

"Ta."

Bill sniffed the aromatic brew (but not too closely) and sipped with self-evident relish.

"God blimey, that was a narrow squeak I've just had with that new young copper who patrols Westminster Road."

"Well take your hat and coat off and tell us about it."

Bill took his coat off but kept his hat on.

Sal clasped her hands comfortably across her midriff and settled back in her chair. Wilf looked expectantly at his joker of a son-in-law.

"There's this new young copper see who seems to think he's on to some sort of fiddle and he keeps poking his nose into things that don't concern him."

Bill still managed a hardware shop and shared fire watching duties with neighbouring shopkeepers. Over time, these free traders had established an informal, mutual help co-operative – not only in relation to incendiary bombs but essential war supplies.

"Yes, as I passed him on my way here, I touched my hat and said, 'Good evening Constable.' And he said, 'Good evening sir,' quite matey like."

Bill chuckled heartily at the recollection.

"Well?"

"Well, it's a good job he hadn't got a bird with him. I might have raised my hat."

"Quite right and proper too. What's wrong with that?"

"Well, God blimey – look what's under my hat!"

Bill lifted his trilby to reveal a carefully wrapped package resting on his thinning hair. Chuckling still, he handed the paper package to his mother-in-law.

"It's for you Nan. It's half a pound of bacon. You can let Pop have a rasher or two if you like – and maybe his nibs there," pointing to Jim, "if he behaves himself."

*

"Corn in Egypt," said Pop the following morning at breakfast.

"Corn in Egypt," echoed his son.

"Three cheers for Bill," said Ma, with one rasher less on her own plate.

Despite this wonderfully crisp and crackling boost to morale, doubts, misgivings, anxieties continued to gnaw, just now and then, at Jim's mental and emotional vitals.

"Julie certainly is a nice girl, I wonder – but no, I am frightened of being hurt again – or am I? Almost forgot. Letter from Mary, but not a very heartening one."

That near oversight occurred just a few days after Britain's worst air raid of the war – the devastating raid on Coventry which signified new tactics by the Luftwaffe -to destroy specific industrial cities: "five hundred planes believed to have taken part...must be absolute hell. Julie evacuated. Glad and at same time sorry."

A few days later Birmingham received another 'real pasting' and the following morning; "didn't start work until ten, with everyone talking about their crater. Becomes a little boring after a time."

Jim, "a little washed out", dozily wondered why, no matter what the unpleasant circumstances, people would try and out vie one another – be it in regard to the intensity of toothache pain, the number of stitches in a wound or, as now, the size of 'our bomb crater'.

He was abruptly jolted out of that doze by a "bomb falling near. Exploded as it touched the roof. Not much damage, save for a lot of broken glass."

This was getting a bit too thick with daylight raids now. Something would have to be done.

One of the worst features of an air raid, for Jim, was frustration – the damnable inability to hit back at the attacker. People naturally varied in their reactions to the sound of bombs falling and exploding- grin and bear it attitudes, grim-lipped silence, assumed jocularity, wearied resignation, and so on. But no single individual could hit back – except with words. No, something would have to be done, if only symbolically.

It was. On 22nd November 1940, not one of the war's notable turning point dates, but important nevertheless for one individual's morale – Jim, on a sudden impulse, joined the Home Guard, the Hopes' Company of the South Staffs.

In best music hall style, Jim was only partially kitted out – tunic and trousers, but not serge; anti-gas ointment and field dressing – but no boots; "smallest size in stock a large nine, much too big for my dainty feet." 'There's a war on you know.'

Indeed there was, "main water pipe from Wales is broken. Queues for water, all water has to be boiled. As a precautionary measure against typhoid, all children being evacuated." May and young Bill went to stay with Aunt Mabel in the Black Country.

Parades and guard duty began at the factory. "Barrack room language is certainly vile, still I suppose one must take the rough with the smooth and turn a deaf ear."

Jim wondered whether he was a prude. No, on reflection, he didn't really think so. In all the homes he knew, his own, those of relatives and friends, in Birmingham, the Black Country, Stroud – he had never experienced 'effin and blindin'. The occasional 'bugger' or 'bloody' might be used but nothing stronger. No, he found it odd, boring and a little sad, this endless stream of obscenities of the guard room.

The men themselves, factory floor workers mostly, were good natured enough and hard working – but did not look after their language in the attentive way they looked after their machines – or come to that, their rifles which had to be kept 'clean, bright and slightly oiled.'

In his own mind, and usually when he was on guard duty, Jim continued to grapple with the apparent paradox that certain parts of the body, employed in the right manner at the right time, could achieve the highest level of ecstasy known to man – and yet be used, in descriptive terms, to convey the greatest – insults, depths of anger and hate. A weird business altogether.

No, Jim could enjoy 'rudery' if it had a bit of wit about it, a touch of style. He chuckled as he recalled a recent guardroom incident.

Guard duties were usually allocated on a two hours on duty, four hours off basis – a guard commonly being mounted at 6 p.m. and standing down at 6 a.m. This entailed two turns of duty of two hours for each man. For most squaddies, the middle guard 8 – 10 p.m. and 2 – 4 a.m. was the least popular, being the most disruptive to kipping patterns.

"Smith, I'm telling you, it is your turn tonight to take the second guard again."

"Are you sure sarge?"

"Dead sure. I've just checked again. Justice must be done and be seen to be done."

As the disgruntled Private Smith clumped away, he was heard to mutter, "Well, if that's justice, my prick's a kipper – and I don't smell fish!"

*

The interrupted pattern of life continued – sort of hand in hand with emotional unease. With Julie away and Dave still hot footing it after Hilda, Jim was drawn increasingly into Ellen's company. Her table tennis improved and his speed of response to her dry Scottish wisecracks steadily increased. Fair-haired Ellen of the twinkling eye and slightly roguish smile. She was so easy to talk to about matters great and small – how to chassé in the quickstep, and the future of the world.

After the air raid of 11/12th December, Jim was mightily relieved to find he still had a future.

While in bed in the house, he suddenly awoke from a doze during a raid, to hear his parents arguing in agitated voices downstairs. Jim put on his slippers and went to join them.

"I don't care what you say Wilf, I'm going."

"It's sheer madness. And you know I can't come with you, not with my gammy leg. I can't keep pace with you at the best of times, and now, now you've worked yourself into this state..."

Wilf flung up his arms in exasperation and near despair, turning with deeply troubled face to his son.

"I can't make your mother see sense son. See what you can do."

"Why, what's the matter?"

"Well, you know that very loud bang which brought you out of bed earlier tonight?"

"The one that blew out part of our front window?"

"Yes. Your mom's got it into her head that it was a land mine and that it exploded near her brothers."

"I think it was much nearer to Handsworth Wood myself – Jerry was probably trying to hit the railway lines."

"I agree, but your mom just won't have it. She insists on going to find out whether her brothers are safe."

"And I shall be off in a minute." Sal's face was deeply flushed.

Jim knew that it was not a scrap of good arguing with his mother when she was in such a state. Her overpowering maternal instincts would not be abated by any rational argument.

Sal went to fetch her topcoat hanging near the pantry.

"Hang on just a tick Ma, while I get dressed. I'm coming with you."

Jim made for the stairs.

Mother and son stepped into the road and hurried along. No one was about on this clear, still night. Not a tin hat in sight. Gun flashes regularly lit up the sky. Noise, ugly noise reverberated all around – droning bombers, exploding bombs, anti-aircraft shells bursting and raining down jagged shrapnel. This pattered heavily on the pavements, roads and roofs. Jim thought – 'how bloody daft if we get wounded or killed by our own side.'

"Come on Mom, this shrapnel's getting far too heavy. We'll have to shelter a minute. Here, let's use this car."

The car, parked by the kerb, had its windows open. Sal and Jim thrust their heads and shoulders inside, trusting to luck for the safety of what remained outside the 'shelter.' (A grotesquely amusing sight thought Jim later – hope it upset the enemy bomb aimer.)

"Come on son, let's make a dash for it."

Sal still fretted and without waiting for Jim's agreement quickly moved on, half walking, half trotting to her brothers' homes. All safe and sound and greatly astonished to see such a pair of 'orphans of the storm' turning up amid the showers of shrapnel.

"Just like our Sal," murmured Uncle Sam as he made, with practised old soldier's hand, large cups of tea, generously laced with rum for the totally unexpected visitors.

Another 'squeak' that same day for Jim. He had to cycle home by a different route from the one taken to work as a UXB had been found during the day. 'Good job,' he thought, 'that it hadn't gone off during his yawning ride to work. Still, it was one way of getting to know more about some of Birmingham's outer suburbs.' Trouble again though with his bike – first a wobbling wheel and then a broken chain. Not much fun trying to mend things in the blackout with some rain always getting inside your oilskins.

But what an antidote for the blues, an evening at the Social Centre, with billiards, table tennis and amusing anecdotes, told in breezy, chuckling manner by Ellen, anecdotes about her past experiences as a telephone operator. All good fun and warm-hearted fellowship, excepting some of the bizarre phone calls.

With the bike temporarily out of action, Jim found the loss of independence and travelling to and from work on the bus "very miserable and depressing." A Christmas card from Mary brought some cheer: "...basket of roses, with 'Remembrances' written underneath. Only wish we could go about together again. Damn...I can't make up my mind."

Christmas Day and after the morning church service; "Ellen took us [Dave and Jim] to her house...father very nice. 1917 port very nice too." Boxing Day, back at work for half a day then a visit to the palatial Paramount, up town; "Wish I could take Julie here."

It was Julie, now temporarily returned to Brum, who gave Jim the words of a song that had recently become popular: 'All the Things You Are.'

"You are the promised kiss of springtime,
That makes the lonely winter seem long...
The dearest things I know are what you are..."

This was a consolation prize for Jim having missed the last waltz with Julie the evening before, "Dave having swiped it...the cad."

Yes, a pretty song 'All the things you are' but one to be sung by a feller to a girl – with its references to 'angel glow' and suchlike. But sung to which girl?

"Some day my happy arms will hold you ..."

But which "you" for heaven's sake?

Battered old 1940 was coming to an end. The decision could easily be deferred to next year. In any case, was he being big headed? Jim reviewed the evidence.

Neither Julie nor Ellen had given any sign that his company was unwelcome to them. And Mary? He had only to think back to the days of bluebells and hey nonino, the tender parting at Worcester station, and her letters – for a warmly reassuring answer.

Julie was prettier but Ellen was wittier. Demure, doe-eyed Julie – but hang on, he felt sure a hint of gentle mischief lurked in those large, "innocent" eyes. And Ellen – a gal with a great sense of humour: she'd always be good company and a great pal. And Mary– oh hell, had she still been living in Cherry Orchard, there would have been no confusion in his thoughts and emotions. Of that he was sure.

For Jim, Mary had that spark of magic that made the difference between *the* girl and other charmers.

Perhaps when winter was past, he'd make a more determined effort to cycle to see her.

Perhaps he'd make up his mind on the basis of the first of the three who would be the next girl to kiss him, and, as a bit of insurance, on the quality of the kiss, better still, kisses. Mary had provided a good yardstick by which to judge such finely balanced romantic matters.

Thoughts like these flickered through Jim's mind as he started to get ready for the dance. He picked up his 1940 diary. Fancy, he'd not been given a diary for 1941. But then, his schooldays were behind him. Chub would have a good laugh if he could read what his gift from last year now contained. Should he take his diary with him to the dance? No, better not. It was a bit bulky and would spoil the outline of his smart, new, cheerful green, tweed sports jacket, which looked pretty nifty with the burnt orange coloured shirt and pearl grey slacks.

He carefully put the diary alongside its 1938 and 1939 companions, in the small front compartment of his old school satchel. He'd complete the 1940 diary later. He'd have a dance to report on, for one thing. And maybe it would be back to the good old days of * * *.

And what a super hop that was.

'H'm there's something in the air tonight' and not just the heady mix of glowing youth, 'Californian Poppy' and 'Evening in Paris', but 'H'm There's Romance in the Air.'

*

Well before the last waltz, Jim slipped away into the darkness, gun flashes flickering far in the distance. Blast, they would be in the direction he was making for.

"Oh Jim, I'm so glad you were able to get here, especially on such a night."

Such fragrance! And such a spine-tingling, toe-curling kiss. There wasn't much to be said but plenty of good reasons for clinging together.

"Come on, I'd better see you home before the raid gets any worse."

A breathless half walk, half trot, then, "See you next year – do take care."

Another toe curler.

"You bet!"

Jim started off at a good steady mile pace towards Handsworth. As the pandemonium increased, he suddenly dived into a sheltering entry. A blinding flash of light – a vicious, searing blast of air, an ear splitting crash. Diary days were at an end.